S0-BZR-329
Spooky stuff
Creepy stuff
Ex Libris
YOUR NAME
ART
BEWARE OF WHAT LIES INSIDE

Parfait Press
An imprint of the Baker & Taylor Publishing Group
10350 Barnes Canyon Road, San Diego, CA 92121

ISBN-13: 978-1-60710-822-1
ISBN-10: 1-60710-822-4

Manufactured, printed, and assembled in Guangdong, China.
1 2 3 4 5 17 16 15 14 13

Q: What is a mummy's favorite flower?
A: Chrysanthemummy

PROF. Zacharias Zog's

Splat-A-Fact™

DOODLES
DOT-TO-DOTS
PUZZLES!
MAZES
ART
COOL STUFF
DOODLES
STUFF
SPOT THE DIFFERENCES

SPOOKY Activity Book

by

Prof. Zacharias Zog

and

Prof. Your name

Which bandage will unravel the mummy?
Q: Why don't mummies go on vacation?
joke!

A: They're afraid they will relax and unwind!

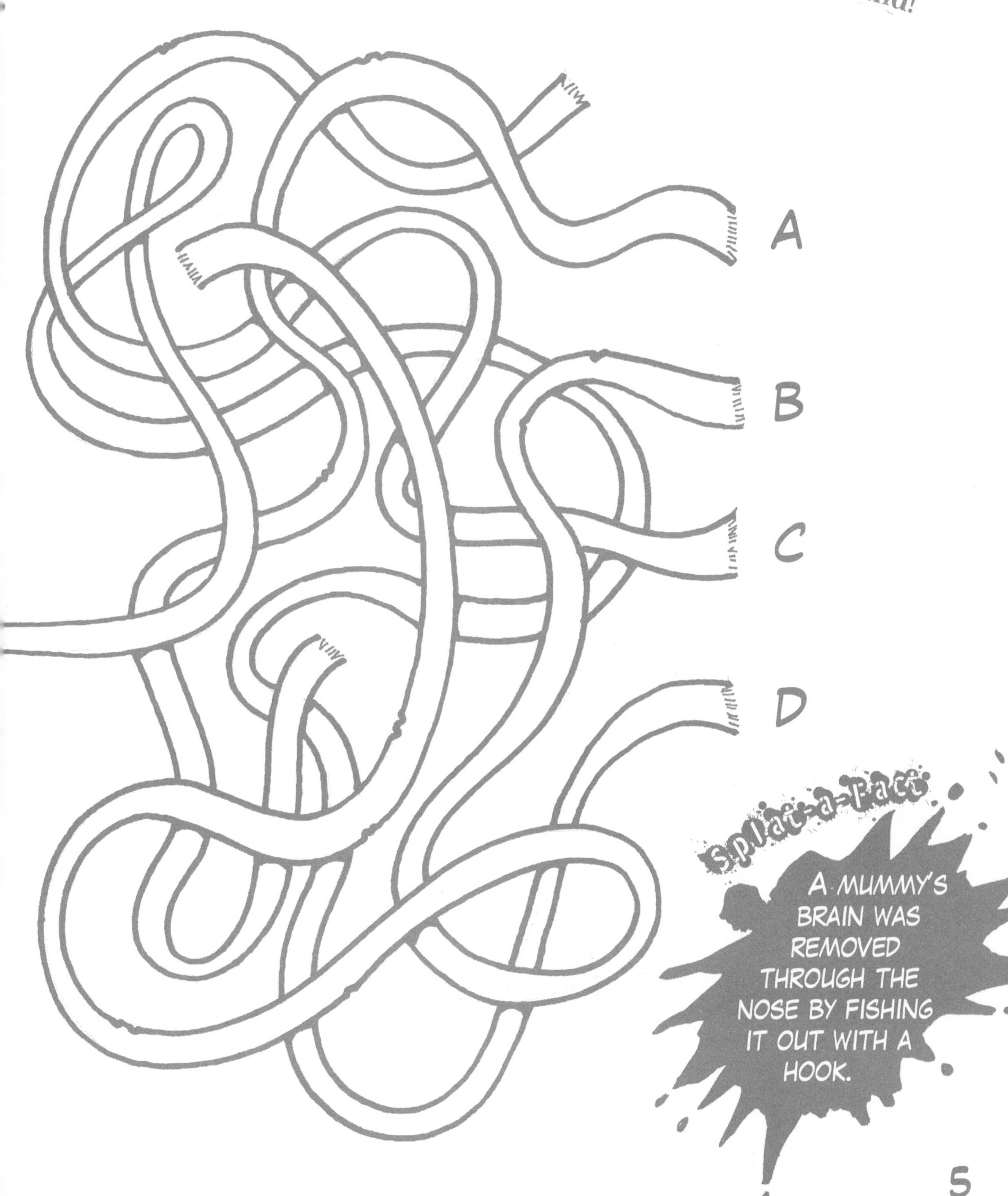

Color in this flying witch and her cat

Which button brings the creature to life?

A

B

C

D

Splat-a-Fact
FRANKENSTEIN WAS WRITTEN BY MARY SHELLEY IN 1818.

Can you find two that are the same?
1
2
3
joke!
Q: What is black, white, and orange and waddles?

A: A penguin carrying a pumpkin!

4

NOW COLOR THEM IN!

5

6

Splat-a-Fact

A PUMPKIN IS A MEMBER OF THE CUCURBITA FAMILY, WHICH INCLUDES SQUASH AND CUCUMBERS.

Fit all the words into the crossword

BLACK

HALLOWEEN

DRACULA

HAUNTED

MUMMY

CAT

TOADS

B
A
T

Creepy Crossword

Splat-a-Fact

Halloween is always celebrated on October 31 and is known by other names such as All Hallows' Eve, Samhain, All Hallowtide, The Feast of the Dead and Day of the Dead.

VAMPIRE

SCREAM

COSTUME

TREAT

TRICK

LITTLE DEVIL

Help the Little Devil find his candy

Trick or treat?

Splat-a-Fact

In 2009, the most popular Halloween character for adults and children was Michael Jackson.

CANDY

Splat-a-Fact

The very first jack o' lantern was made out of hollowed-out turnips.

Bat Attack!

MWA
HA
HA
HA
HA

CAN YOU FIND ANY PAIRS OF MATCHING BAT SILHOUETTES?
SPLAT-A-FACT
BECAUSE VAMPIRE BATS ARE SO SMALL, THEY CANNOT STORE MUCH ENERGY FROM THEIR FOOD. UNLESS THEY EAT EVERY TWO TO THREE DAYS, THEY WILL DIE. SO IF A BAT BECOMES TOO WEAK TO FLY, OTHER MEMBERS OF THE COLONY WILL REGURGITATE THEIR FOOD TO FEED IT.
SPLAT-A-FACT
A VAMPIRE BAT DRINKS BLOOD FROM COWS, PIGS AND HORSES (AND THE OCCASIONAL HUMAN). THEIR SALIVA CONTAINS A SPECIAL CHEMICAL THAT MIXES WITH ANIMAL BLOOD TO KEEP IT FROM CLOTTING AND MAKE IT FLOW FREELY.

Find the two identical Vampire Kids!

C
D
E
F

Count the spots

joke!

Q: What did one pumpkin say to the other pumpkin?

Splat-a-Fact

THERE ARE NO WORDS IN THE DICTIONARY THAT RHYME WITH "ORANGE."

A: Cut it out!
THE MUTANT PUMPKIN HAS 7 MORE SPOTS IN THIS PICTURE. CAN YOU FIND THEM?

Splat-a-Fact

GHOSTS DO NOT SLEEP, AND WHEN A GHOST ENTERS A ROOM, THE ROOM USUALLY GETS COLD.

NOISY, TROUBLESOME GHOSTS ARE KNOWN AS POLTERGEISTS.

Escape the maze without crossing a ghost!

Pick up the bone that is on top of the pile each time, until you reach the bottom
D
A
B
C
PICK UP THE BONES!

E
G
F

Spot the differences 1

joke!

Q: What kind of ship does Dracula sail on?

Splat-a-Fact

VAMPIRES ARE IMMORTAL AND THEY HAUNT THE WORLD OF THE LIVING, LONGING FOR FRESH BLOOD.

A: A blood vessel!

Finish drawing the two werewolves

Spot the differences 2

Splat-a-Fact

DEATH, OR "THE GRIM REAPER," ALWAYS CARRIES A SCYTHE.

Write your own comic strip

Splat-a-Fact

THE MOST HAUNTED HOUSE IS "THE HOUSE OF HORROR" IN AMITYVILLE, NEW YORK.

DON'T FORGET
TO ADD SPEECH
BUBBLES!

Color in the picture and count how much candy the vampire has!
THEY DON'T CALL ME "COUNT" DRACULA FOR NOTHING!

Can you un-jumble these spooky words?

OKPSOS

_ _ _ _ _ _ _

MNAHPTO

_ _ _ _ _ _ _

THGSOS

_ _ _ _ _ _

TSIIPR

_ _ _ _ _ _

oooooooohhh

G L U O H S

_ _ _ _ _ _

R E P C E S

_ _ _ _ _ _

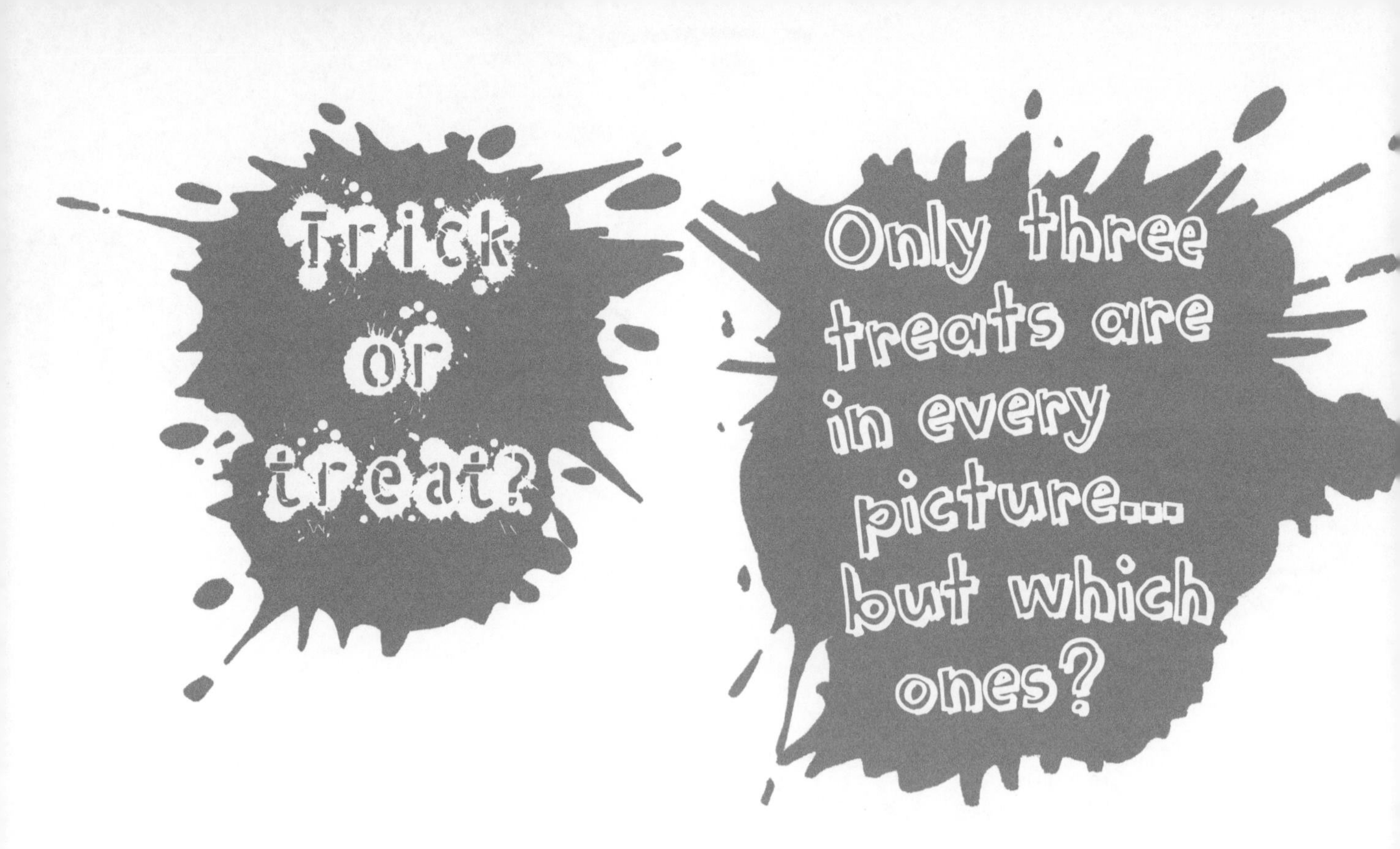
Trick or treat?
Only three treats are in every picture... but which ones?

Draw faces on the pumpkins

joke!

Q: What is a pumpkin's favorite sport?

A: Squash!

Join the dots 1

Splat-a-Fact

Bobbing for apples is thought to have originated from the Roman harvest festival that honors Pamona, the goddess of fruit trees.

hissssssss

Splat-a-Fact

SNAKES HAVE BETWEEN 100-400 VERTEBRAE WITH AS MANY RIBS ATTACHED! THAT IS WHAT MAKES THEM SO FLEXIBLE AND HELPS THEM TO MOVE ALONG!

Splat-a-Fact

THE OWL IS A POPULAR HALLOWEEN IMAGE. IN MEDIEVAL EUROPE, OWLS WERE THOUGHT TO BE WITCHES, AND TO HEAR AN OWL'S CALL MEANT SOMEONE WAS ABOUT TO DIE.

Write your own spell!

Magic Spell Recipe

Ingredients:

1 frog

Method:

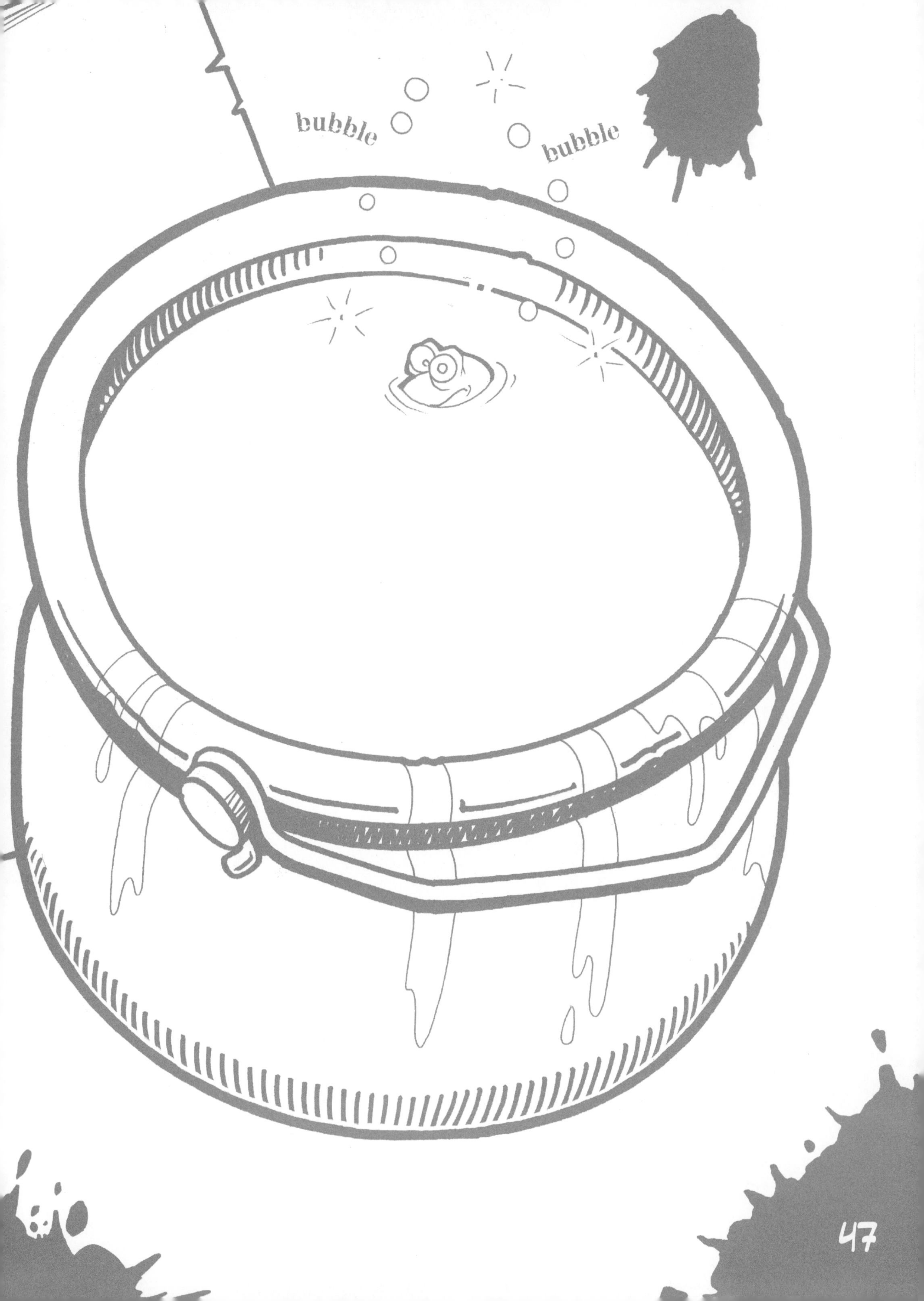
bubble
bubble

What a witch!

Q: Which school subject are witches best at?

joke!

SAMHAINOPHOBIA IS A PHOBIA OF HALLOWEEN.

Splat-a-Fact

FILL IN THE WITCH'S DETAIL
A: Spelling!
cackle!
Splat-a-Fact
THE FIRST MASS-PRODUCED HALLOWEEN COSTUMES APPEARED IN THE 1930S IN THE USA.

Can you spot me hiding in the dark?
HOW MANY MONSTERS ARE WITH ME?

Join
the dots
2
1
2
3
4
5
6
7
8
9
10
11
12
13
14
15
16
17
18
19
20
21
22
23
24
25
26
27
28
29
30
31
32
33
34
35
36
37
38
39
40
41
42
43
44
45
46
47
48
49
50
51
52
53
54
55
56

It is said that a werewolf can only be killed by a silver bullet, and that women werewolves have poisonous claws and can kill children just by looking at them!
Splat-a-Pace

Help the monster find his eyes

Splat-a-Fact
THE CYCLOPS WAS A ONE-EYED GIANT WHO SCOOPED MEN UP AND ATE THEM ALIVE.
I SEE YOU!

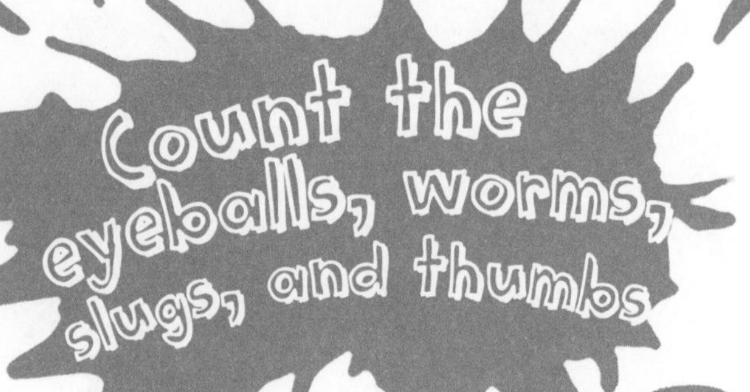

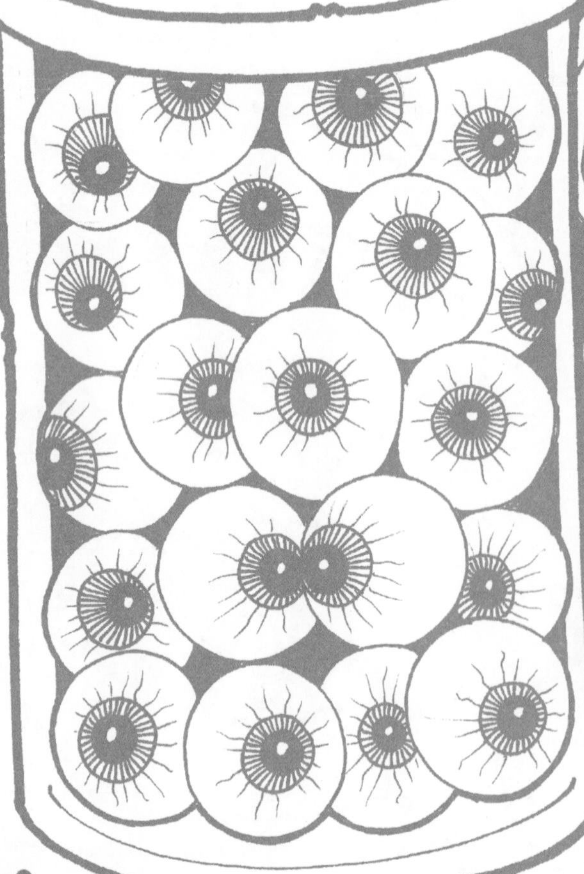

There are over fifty different types of pumpkin. They have such great names as the Spooktacular, the Funny Face and the Munchkin.

Splat-a-Fact

Yuk!

ROMAN MYTHS TOLD HOW THE STRIX (SCREECH OWL) WAS ONCE A WOMAN, BUT SHE ATE HUMAN FLESH AND BLOOD, AND BECAME A VAMPIRE BIRD.
Splat-a-Fact
erm.....
ummmm...

How to draw Frankenstein's monster

Splat-a-Draw

Splat-a-Fact

VICTOR FRANKENSTEIN WAS A FICTIONAL MEDICAL STUDENT WHO OBSERVED HOW BODIES DECAYED.

3
4
Splat-a-Fact
PUMPKINS
CAN BE BLUE,
GREEN OR WHITE, AS
WELL AS THE
TRADITIONAL ORANGE!

Creating creepy characters

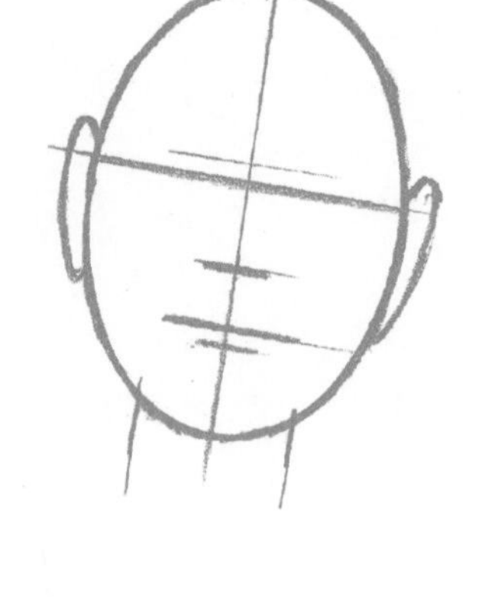

Draw in an oval head shape and mark in the position of the facial features with construction lines.

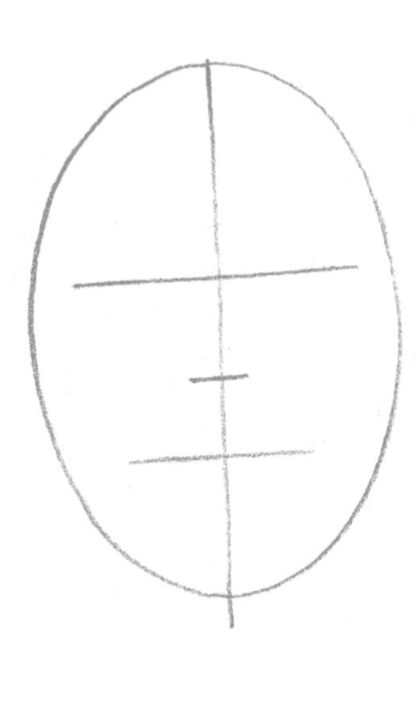

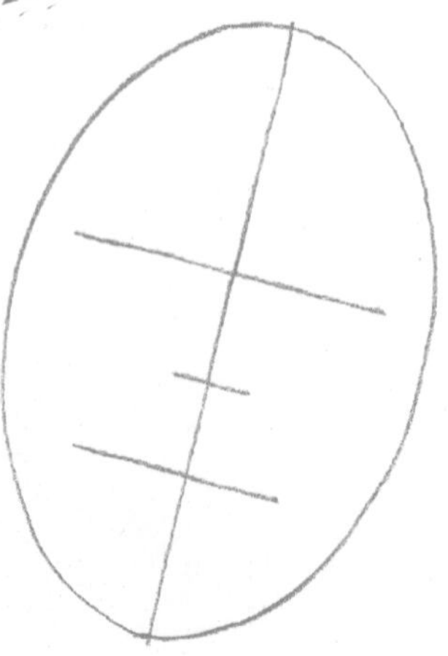

100% spooky
ADD FEROCIOUS TEETH, A SPOOKY HAT OR DEVILISH HORNS TO CREATE A NEW CHARACTER.

WORD SEARCH 1
FIND ALL 10 OF US IN THE WORD SEARCH!
MONSTER
BAT
TOAD
WEREWOLF
VAMPIRE
MUMMY
WITCH
RAT
SKELETON
SPIDER
Q: Why didn't the skeleton dance at the party?
joke!

Splat-a-Fact GREED AND VIOLENCE ARE A VAMPIRE'S ONLY PLEASURES; THEY DO NOT CARE HOW MANY THEY DEVOUR TO GET FRESH BLOOD. LOATHED AND FEARED, THEY ARE OUTCASTS FOREVER.

Y	W	O	P	B	E	R	I	M
L	I	E	T	S	A	E	N	U
R	T	R	R	K	C	T	E	M
E	C	I	P	E	Q	S	H	M
D	H	P	U	L	W	N	E	Y
I	L	M	S	E	D	O	R	F
P	L	A	S	T	R	M	L	K
S	C	V	T	O	A	D	R	F
R	Y	E	R	N	T	A	A	O

A: He had no body to dance with!

Find the words hidden in the grid

Make Halloween treats

MARSHMALLOW

SWEETS

LICORICE

Creepy Craft
LIME
Jelly
+
RED LICORICE BOOTLACES
+
RAISINS
Squashed fly and worm soup
Yum!

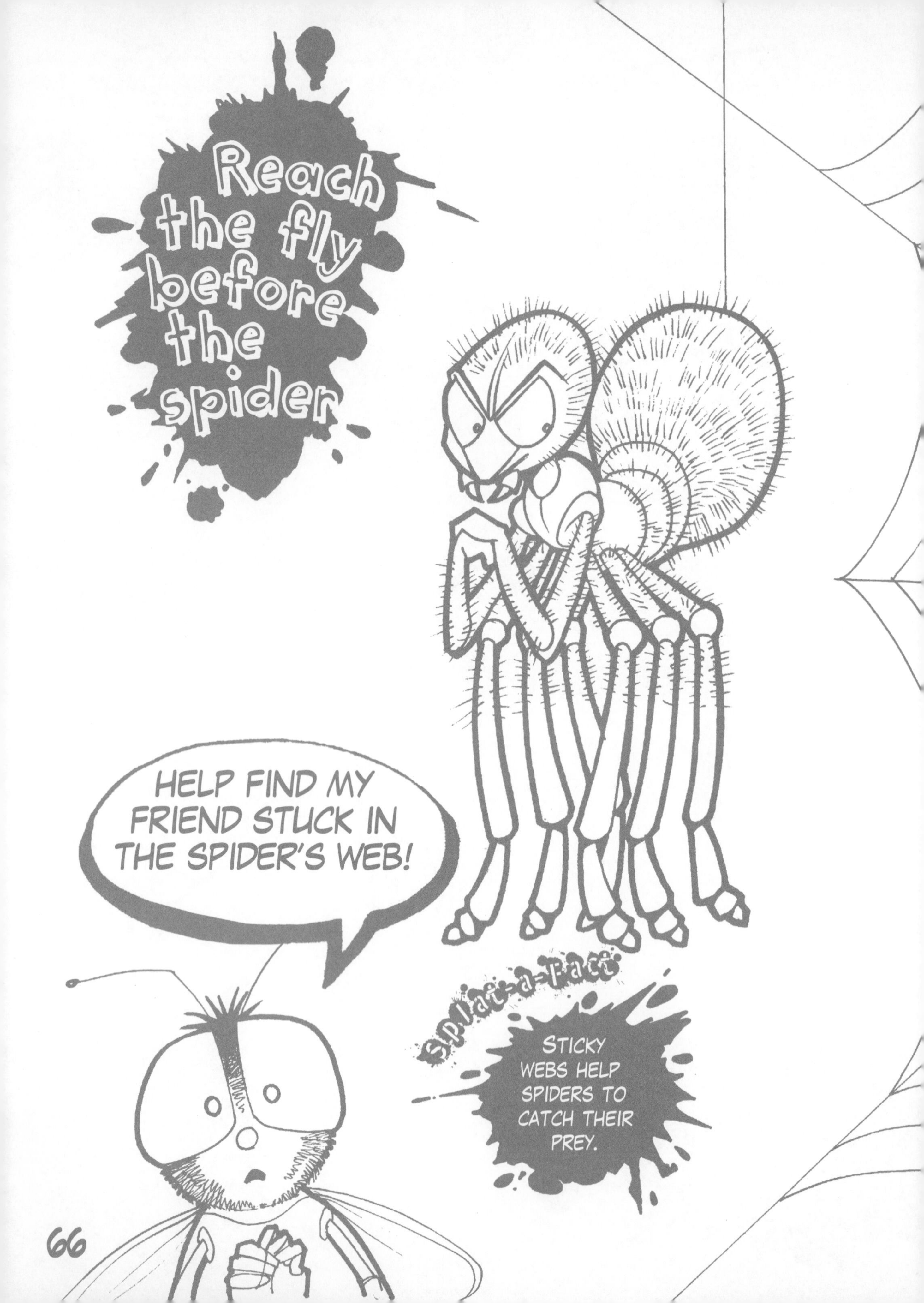
Reach the fly before the spider
HELP FIND MY FRIEND STUCK IN THE SPIDER'S WEB!
Splat-a-Fact
STICKY WEBS HELP SPIDERS TO CATCH THEIR PREY.

A
B
C

Color in the picture to see what the children see
Q: How does a witch tell the time?
joke!
COLOR CODE
1 = DARK BLUE
2 = LIGHT BLUE
3 = BLACK

A: With a witch watch!

Splat-a-Fact

BATS ARE THE ONLY MAMMALS NATURALLY CAPABLE OF TRUE AND SUSTAINED FLIGHT.

How many bats are in the Bat Box?

Mwahahahaha!

COLOR IN THE SHAPES WITHOUT DOTS TO FIND OUT!

Splat-a-Bat

Q: How did the monster cure his sore throat?
joke!

Splat-a-fact

HALLOWEEN IN WELSH IS "NOS CALAN GAEAF."

Draw in the missing parts of the monster

A: He spent all day gargoyling!

Unscramble the words

LDOCARUN

_ _ _ _ _ _ _ _

BKOO FO LELSSP

_ _ _ _   _ _   _ _ _ _ _ _

BCALK TCA

_ _ _ _ _   _ _ _

I'm the cat's whiskers at anagrams!

YFINLG TCWIH

_ _ _ _ _ _   _ _ _ _ _

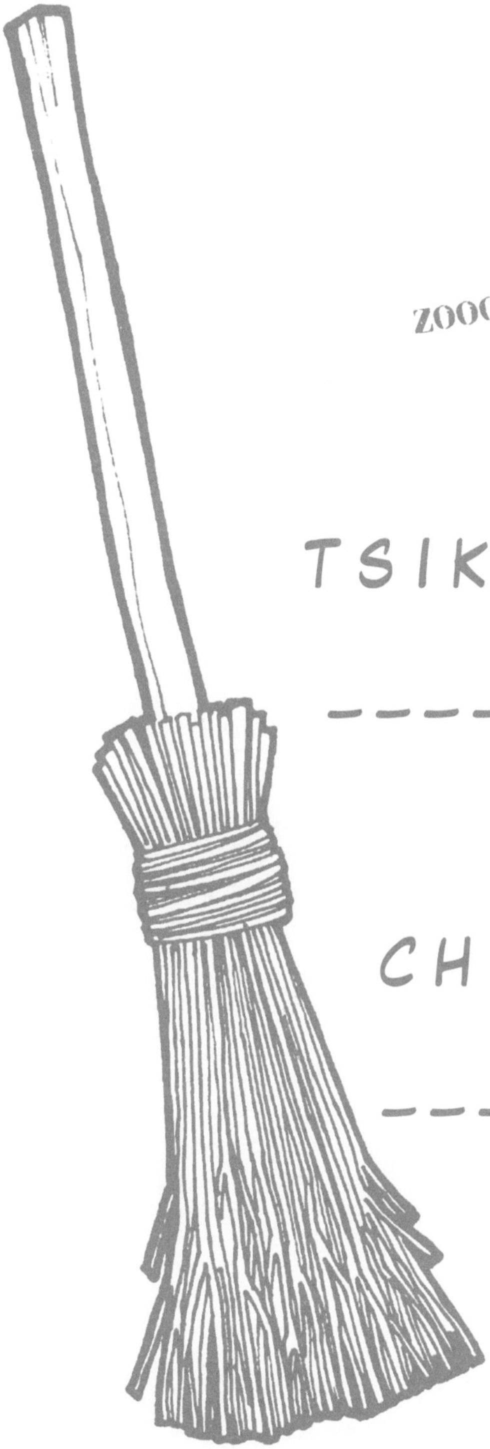

zooooom

TSIKOMOBRC

_ _ _ _ _ _ _ _ _ _

CHITWS THA

_ _ _ _ _ _   _ _ _

Help the rat to find his fleas

Q: How do you start an insect race?
joke!
A: One, two, flea ... go!

It is thought that the colors orange and black became Halloween colors because orange is associated with harvests (Halloween marks the end of harvest) and black is associated with death.
Splat-a-Fact
To meet a witch, put your clothes on inside out and walk backwards on Halloween night.
Splat-a-Lie

Spot the 7 differences
DON'T LOSE YOUR HEAD!

Draw spooky faces on the ghosts!

Oooooooh!
Q: What do you get when you cross Bambi with a ghost?
A: Bamboo!
joke!

Escape from the haunted house!

Splat-a-Fact
THE FASTEST PUMPKIN CARVER IN THE WORLD IS JERRY AYERS OF OHIO. HE CARVED A PUMPKIN IN JUST 37 SECONDS!
C
D
E
B
F
A
Watch out for the ghost!

Only two silhouettes match this bat. Can you find them?
joke!
Q: Why don't bats live alone?
A: They prefer to hang around with their friends!
Splat-a-Fact
IF YOU SEE A SPIDER ON HALLOWEEN, SOME SAY THAT IT COULD BE THE SPIRIT OF A DEAD LOVED ONE WHO IS WATCHING YOU.

A
B
C
D
E
F
G
H

Find these words in the word search:
gargoyle
ghoul
monster
ghost
spook
phantom
zombie
splat-a-search
splat-a-fact
MANY PEOPLE STILL BELIEVE THAT GARGOYLES WERE CREATED BY MEDIEVAL ARCHITECTS AND STONE CARVERS TO WARD OFF EVIL SPIRITS.

A	G	J	O	P	E	W	V	B	C
H	P	E	I	B	M	O	Z	E	G
P	W	H	S	T	N	M	K	E	A
R	K	E	A	C	O	L	O	G	R
Y	L	V	S	N	A	G	O	I	G
E	F	P	S	O	T	H	P	U	O
A	H	T	N	G	H	O	S	T	Y
B	E	R	D	W	Z	U	M	Y	L
R	V	U	I	D	G	L	J	Q	E
T	P	E	H	Z	B	E	S	A	C

HOW TO SPOT A WEREWOLF:
1. CURVED FINGERNAILS
2. EARS LOW ON HEAD
3. EYEBROWS MEET OVER THE NOSE
4. BRISTLES UNDER THE TONGUE
Splat-a-Fact
snarrrrl!
From man to WOLF

Howwwl!
How to draw
a werewolf

DRAW MY CAT WITH THE HELP OF THE GRID!

purrr-fect
drawing

Hiero-glyphs

Walk like an Egyptian

Splat-a-Fact

HIEROGLYPHS, THE EGYPTIAN FORM OF WRITING, WAS CARVED ON TEMPLES AND TOMBS. FOR EVERYDAY WRITING A MORE JOINED-UP FORM WAS USED.

Write like an Egyptian

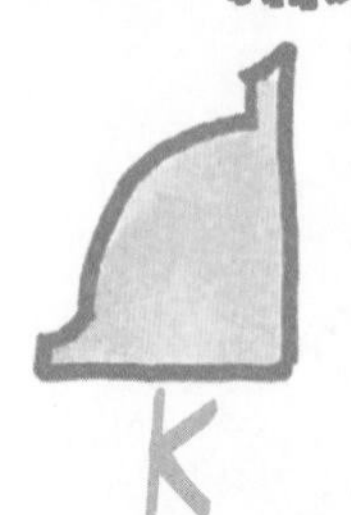

CAN YOU WORK OUT WHAT THE HIEROGLYPHS SAY?

A: The Dead Sea!

Splat-a-Fact
"MASTABA" COMES FROM THE ARABIC WORD FOR "BENCH." IT'S OFTEN A SHAFT OR AN UNDERGROUND BURIAL CHAMBER.
MASTABA TOMB
HORUS
Can the God Horus find the Mastaba Tomb?
A FUNERAL PROCESSION

Curses?
Just add words!
Eeeek!
Splat-a-Fact
HOWARD CARTER DISCOVERED KING TUTANKHAMEN'S TOMB IN 1922 IN THE VALLEY OF THE KINGS, EGYPT. IT WAS SAID THAT THE MUMMY WAS CURSED!

GRRRRR!
Splat-a-Fact
Howard Carter also opened the pharaoh's innermost shrine. But instead of being cursed he lived for another 17 years, and spent 10 of them working on the tomb.

Magic Bricks

N

THE SYMBOL ON THIS BRICK LIVED IN ANCIENT EGYPT

W

THE SYMBOL ON THIS BRICK REPRESENTS STABILITY

E

THE SYMBOL ON THIS BRICK WAS A GOD

THIS BRICK COULD BE LIT

S

splat-a-fact

A SET OF FOUR BRICKS MADE OF MUD, FEATURING DIVINE IMAGES OR SYMBOLS OF GODS, WERE PLACED IN THE TOMB. THESE BRICKS HAD MAGICAL PROPERTIES.

HUMAN FIGURE

DJED AMULET

Match the magic bricks

USING THE CLUES, MATCH THE MAGIC BRICKS TO THE SIDE OF THE TOMB THEY WERE PLACED.

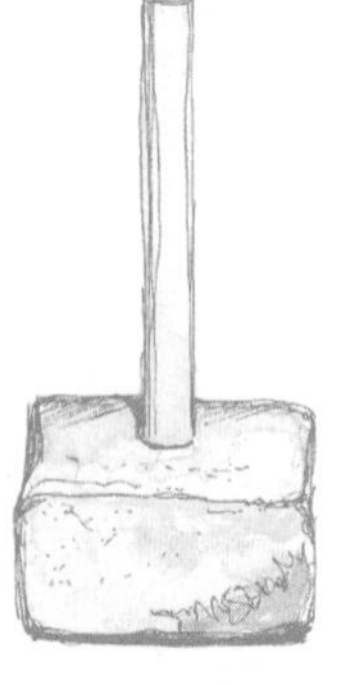

TORCH

CLAY ANUBIS FIGURE

Splat-a-Fact

Canopic jars held the body's organs. The tops of the canopic jars represented the four sons of the god Horus: Imsety, Duamutef, Hapi, and Qebehsenuef.

Canopic Jars

Splat-a-Clue

HUMAN = LIVER

JACKAL = STOMACH

FALCON = INTESTINES

BABOON = LUNGS

MATCH THE ORGANS TO THE JARS

Liver

Lungs

Intestines

Stomach

Bound for the tomb

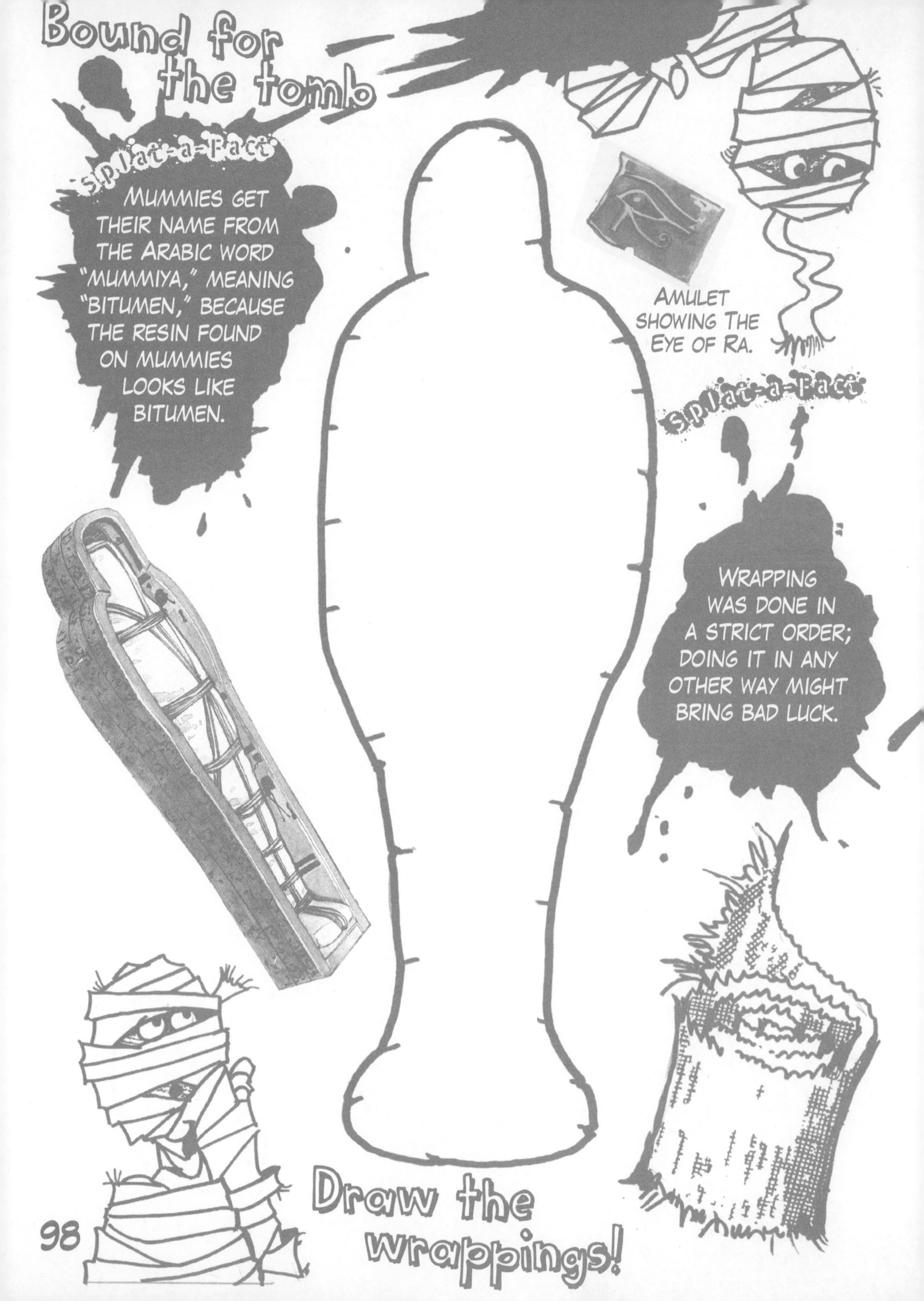

Draw the wrappings!

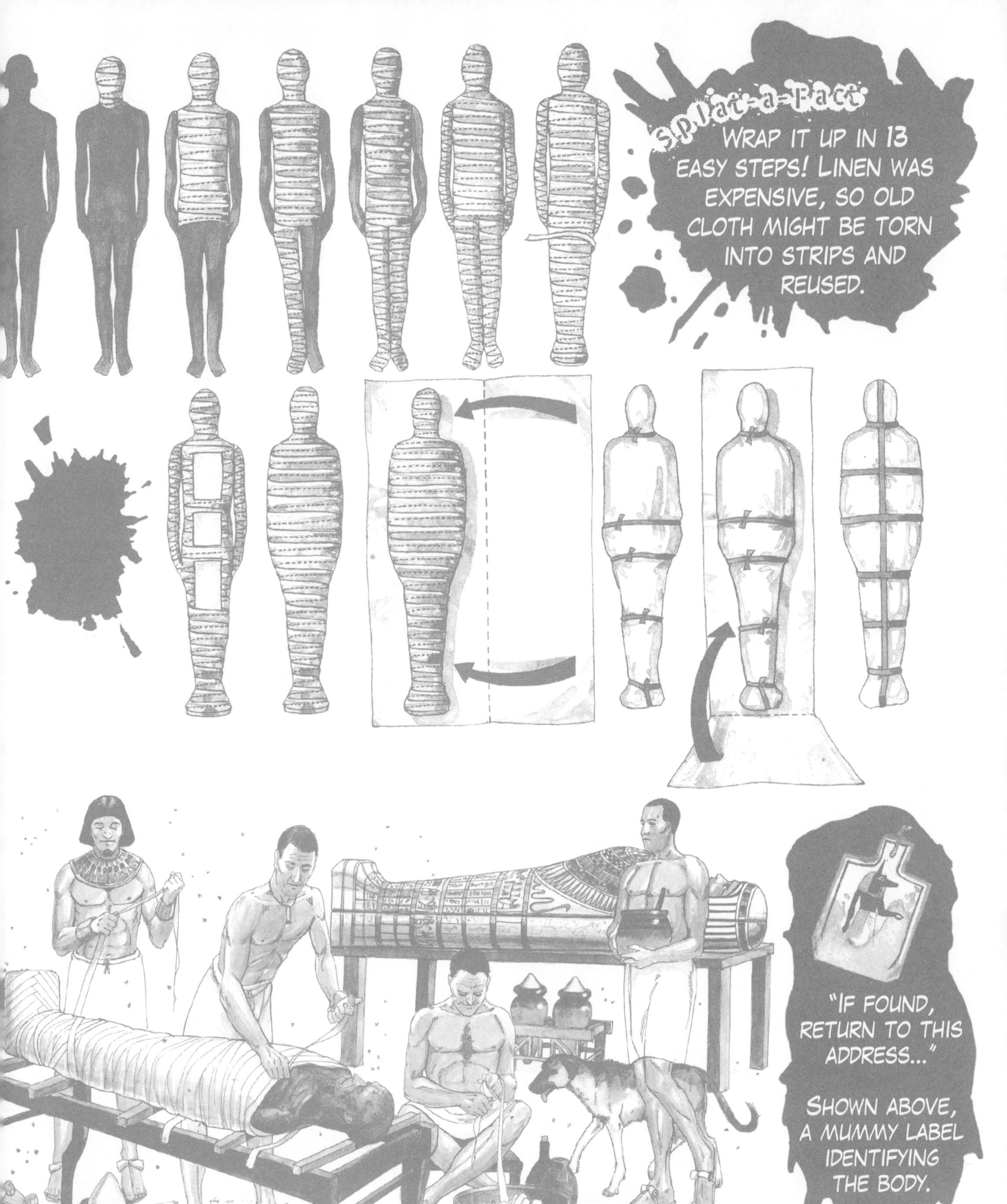
Splat-a-Fact
WRAP IT UP IN 13 EASY STEPS! LINEN WAS EXPENSIVE, SO OLD CLOTH MIGHT BE TORN INTO STRIPS AND REUSED.
"IF FOUND, RETURN TO THIS ADDRESS..."
SHOWN ABOVE, A MUMMY LABEL IDENTIFYING THE BODY.

Splat-a-Fact
To judge from her portrait bust, Akhenaten's chief wife, Queen Nefertiti, was very beautiful.
After the coffin had been carved it was painted with gesso, a mixture of chalk and glue. Then the craftsman pressed on thin sheets of gold.
Splat-a-Fact
Draw Queen Nerfertiti's face and headdress

splat-a-fact
TUTANKHAMEN'S MASK WAS MADE FROM SOLID GOLD.
Joke!
Q: How do you use an Egyptian doorbell?
A: Toot-and-come-in!
Draw Tutankhamen's death mask

Spot the differences
AAARRGGGHHH!
How many differences can you find?

THE BRAIN WAS REMOVED THROUGH THE NOSE BY FISHING IT OUT WITH A HOOK.
Splat-a-Fact
oooohhh
mummy madness

mad mummy math
Mummy Sudoku 1
FILL IN THE NUMBERS 1, 2, 3 AND 4 IN EVERY ROW AND COLUMN.

		3	
			2
2			
4			1

Which way should I go?
During wrapping, amulets were slipped between the linen strips. These would help to protect the dead person in his or her new life.
Mummy Maze
Can you help the Egyptian find his missing amulet?
Scarab amulet

CARPENTERS SHAPED THE COFFIN-CASES, THEN CARVERS ADDED THE DETAILS.
Splat-a-Fact
Can you match all the boxes to the artifacts above?

splat-a-fact
THE EMBALMERS USED FLINT KNIVES TO CUT OPEN THE BODY.
joke!
Q: What kind of music do mummies like?
A: Wrap music!
103% nuts

First, break the seal
Finish decorating the walls of the tomb with paintings.
IN THIS ROOM, DRAW THINGS THAT THE PHARAOH WILL NEED
Q: What did King Tut say when he got scared?
Joke!
A: I want my mummy!
DRAW WHAT'S IN THE SECRET CHAMBER
108

How many scarab beetles can you find?

Add some treasure!

Color in the tomb

Splat-a-Fact

THE FACES ON COFFIN LIDS SHOW AN IDEALIZED HUMAN WAITING FOR THEIR NEW LIFE. THEY ARE NOT PORTRAITS OF THE PERSON INSIDE.

Use a mirror to help you

joke!

Q: What do you say to an annoying scarab?

COLOR IN YOUR DRAWING

A: Stop bugging me!

What are the Egyptians saying?
Make up an Egyptian joke!
THE OPENING OF THE MOUTH CEREMONY REAWAKENED THE MUMMY'S SENSES SO HE OR SHE COULD "LIVE" IN THE NEXT WORLD.
Splat-a-Fact

Ssssss
Help!
FILL IN THE SPEECH BUBBLES

Wrapping it up!

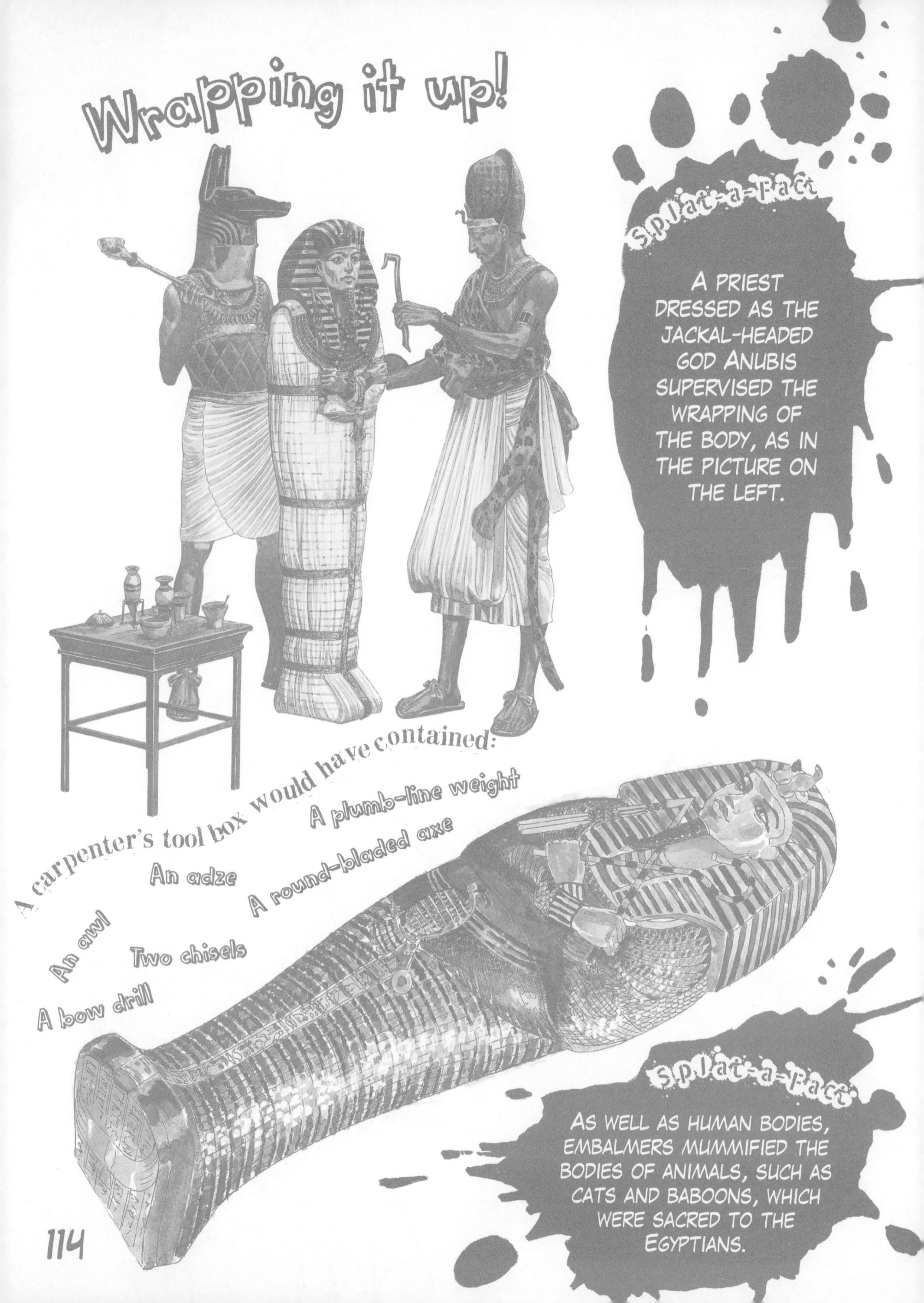

Splat-a-Fact

A PRIEST DRESSED AS THE JACKAL-HEADED GOD ANUBIS SUPERVISED THE WRAPPING OF THE BODY, AS IN THE PICTURE ON THE LEFT.

Splat-a-Fact

AS WELL AS HUMAN BODIES, EMBALMERS MUMMIFIED THE BODIES OF ANIMALS, SUCH AS CATS AND BABOONS, WHICH WERE SACRED TO THE EGYPTIANS.

Splat-a-draw

Can you join the dots to make a mummy mask?

1 2 3 4 5 6 7 8 9 10 11 12 13 14 15 16 17 18 19 20 21 22 23 24 25 26 27 28 29 30 31 32 33 34 35 36 37 38 39 40 41 42 43 44 45 46 47 48 49 50 51 52 53 54 55 56 57 58 59 60 61 62 63 64 65 66 67 68 69 70 71 72 73 74 75 76 77 78 79 80 81 82 83 84 85 86 87 88 89 90 91 92 93 94 95 96 97 98 99 100 101 102 103 104 105 106 107 108 109 110 111 112 113 114 115 116 117 118 119 120 121 122 123 124 125 126 127 128 129

Splat-a-fact

THE BODY WAS COVERED IN NATRON (A TYPE OF NATURAL SALT) AND LEFT TO DRY OUT FOR 40 DAYS.

Draw around your own hand to **create a death mask** on the opposite page

joke!

Q: How did brave Egyptians write?

A: In hero-glyphics!

THE HEART WAS LEFT IN THE BODY SO IT COULD BE JUDGED GOOD OR BAD IN THE NEXT WORLD.

Splat-a-Fact

THE TOMBS OF PHARAOHS WERE SO BIG AND COMPLICATED THAT WORK ON THEM BEGAN LONG BEFORE A PHARAOH DIED. MOST TOOK PART IN PLANNING THEIR OWN TOMB.

Walk like an Egyptian...

How to draw a really scary mummy

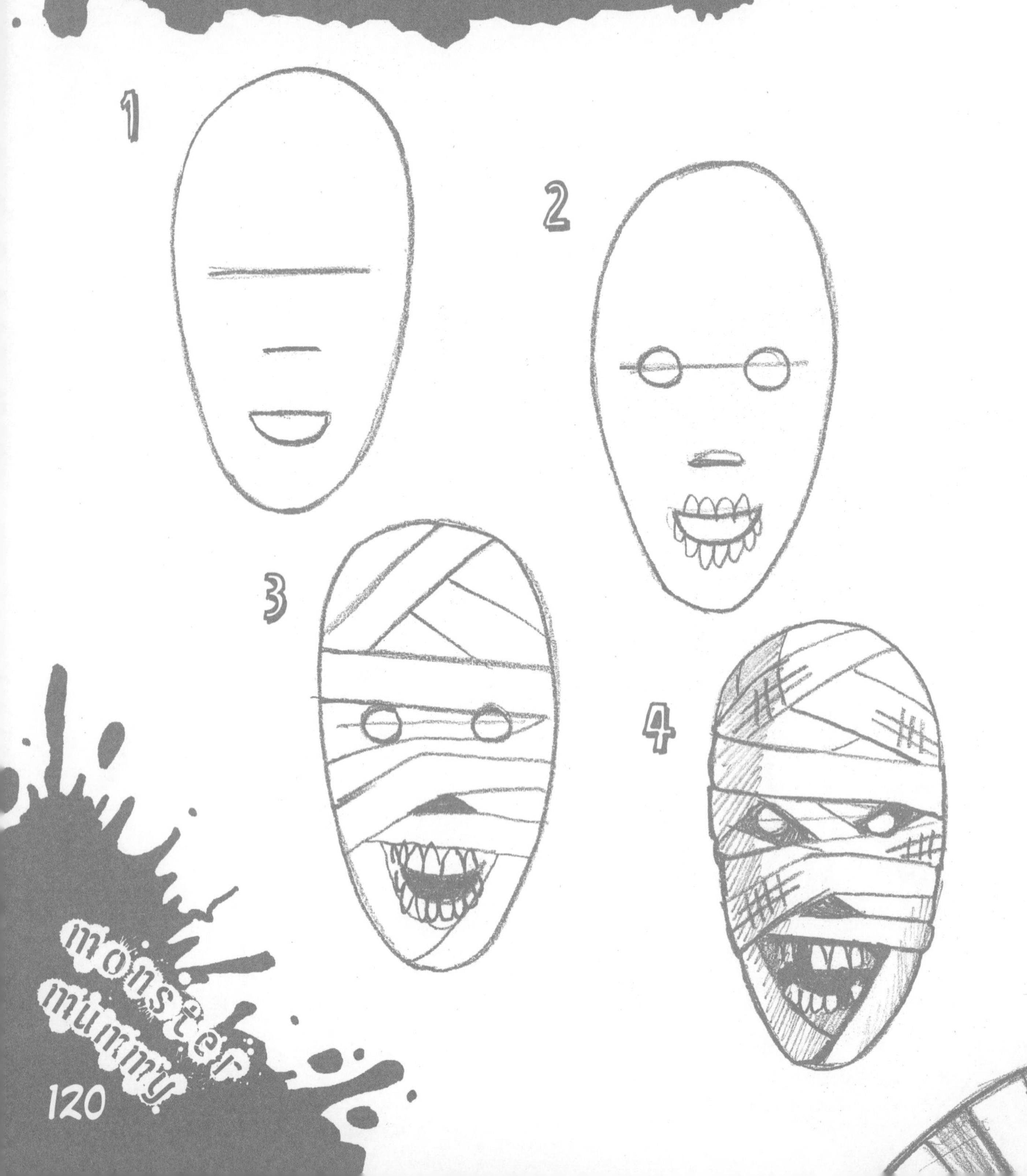

joke!
Q: How did the doctor know that the mummy was ill?
DRAW YOUR OWN MUMMY HERE
A: He was coffin a lot!
GGRRR

How many mummies can you find?

What's the mummy?

Splat-a-Fact

DOGS AND CATS WERE OFTEN MUMMIFIED WITH GREAT CARE AND BURIED WITH THE THINGS THEY WOULD NEED IN THE AFTERLIFE.

Give each mummy a funny name

Color in the crowns
Splat-a-Fact
THE NEMES CROWN HAD A COBRA AND THE HEAD OF A VULTURE TO REPRESENT THE KING'S PROTECTORS.
Splat-a-Fact
THE QUEEN'S HEADDRESS FEATURES NEKHBET, THE VULTURE GODDESS OF UPPER EGYPT.
joke!
Q: What kind of candy do Egyptians eat?

A: Gummy mummies!
Splat-a-Fact
THE KHEPRESH CROWN WAS BRIGHT BLUE AND WAS OFTEN WORN BY PHARAOHS WHO WERE WARRIORS. THE FIRST WAS MADE FOR AMENHOTEP III.
Splat-a-Fact
THE ATEF CROWN WAS OFTEN WORN FOR RELIGIOUS CEREMONIES AND WAS DECORATED WITH TWO OSTRICH FEATHERS.
COLOR THEM IN

Complete the tomb paintings by joining up the dots

COLOR US IN!

WHO WILL WIN?
AAARRGHH
GIVE EACH FIGHTER A NAME AND WRITE ABOUT THEM IN THE BOXES BELOW
LIST THEIR STRENGTHS, WEAKNESSES, POWERS AND WEAPONS

SPLAT-A-BATTLE

FIGHT!

GGRRRRR

Attack of the Mummy Warrior!

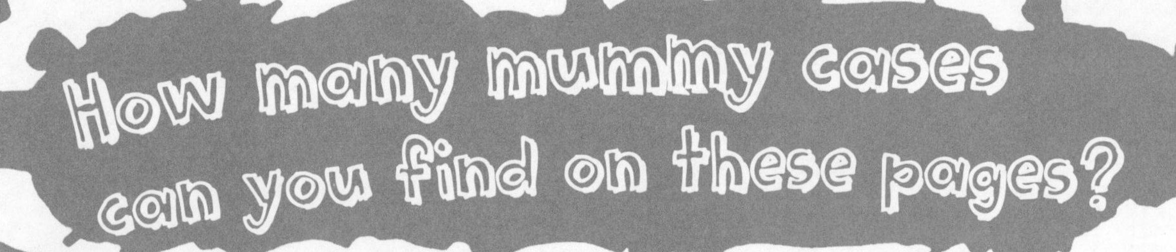

Splat-a-Fact

AN OIL PAINT, CALLED MUMMY BROWN, WAS MANUFACTURED FROM MUMMY PARTS UP UNTIL THE 20TH CENTURY.

97% loopy
USE SIMPLE SHAPES TO DRAW MUMMIES
Splat-a-Fact
WALL PAINTERS HELPED TRANSFER DESIGNS TO THE WALL. BOTH WERE MARKED WITH A GRID. TRAINEES WOULD JUST MIX THE PAINT—POWDER MINERALS AND EGG WHITE OR TREE RESIN.

NOW, YOU HAVE A GO!

CROCODILE
COW
IBIS
COBRA
DOG
CAT
Splat-a-Fact
BABOONS WERE VERY COMMON ANIMALS AND, LIKE THE IBIS, WERE SACRED TO THE GOD THOTH. THE CANOPIC JAR THAT HELD THE LUNGS OF A MUMMIFIED BODY ALWAYS HAD A TOP SHAPED LIKE A BABOON'S HEAD.
LINK THE ANIMALS WITH THEIR MUMMIES

Match the animal to the mummy!

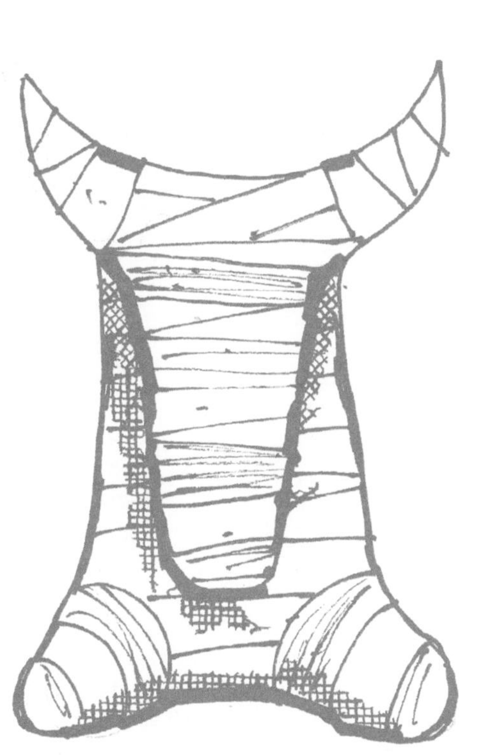

How many mummies can you find in the town?
Splat-a-Fact
THE EMBALMER WOULD SHOW YOUR FAMILY WOODEN MODELS OF VARIOUS STYLES OF MUMMY: CHEAP, MID-RANGE AND LUXURY.

WHERE HAVE THE MUMMIES GONE?

Write the story

THE VALLEY OF THE KINGS WAS REDISCOVERED BY HOWARD CARTER WORKING FOR THE WEALTHY ENGLISHMAN LORD CARNARVON.

Splat-a-Fact

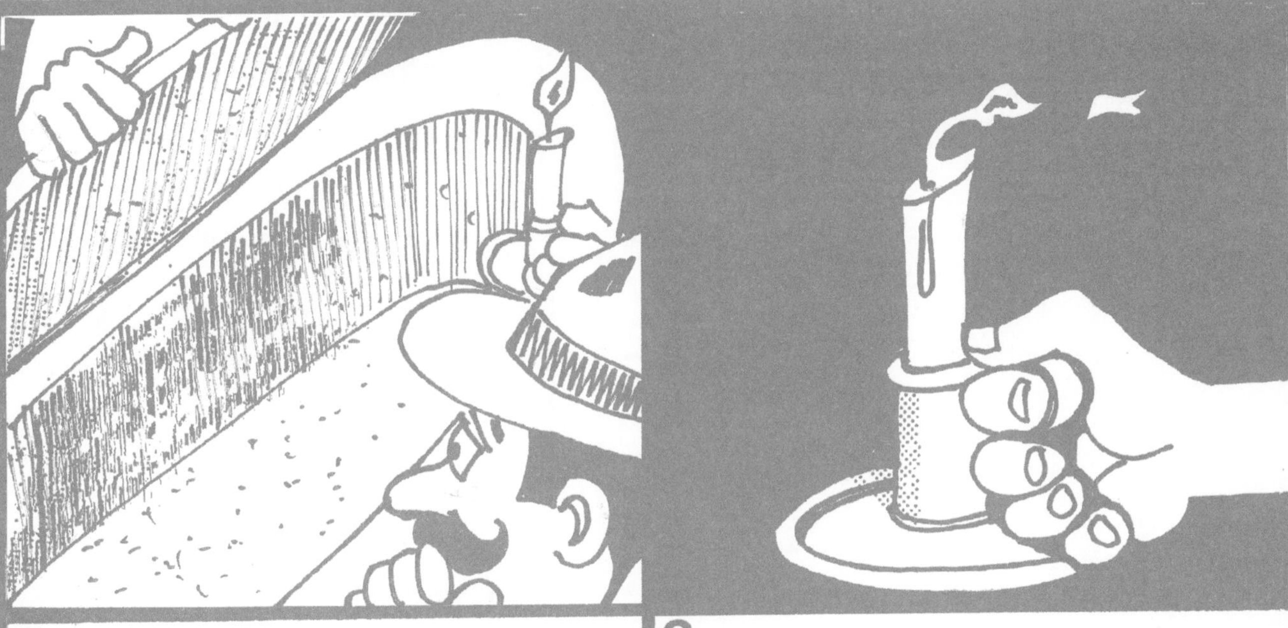

Mummy word search 3

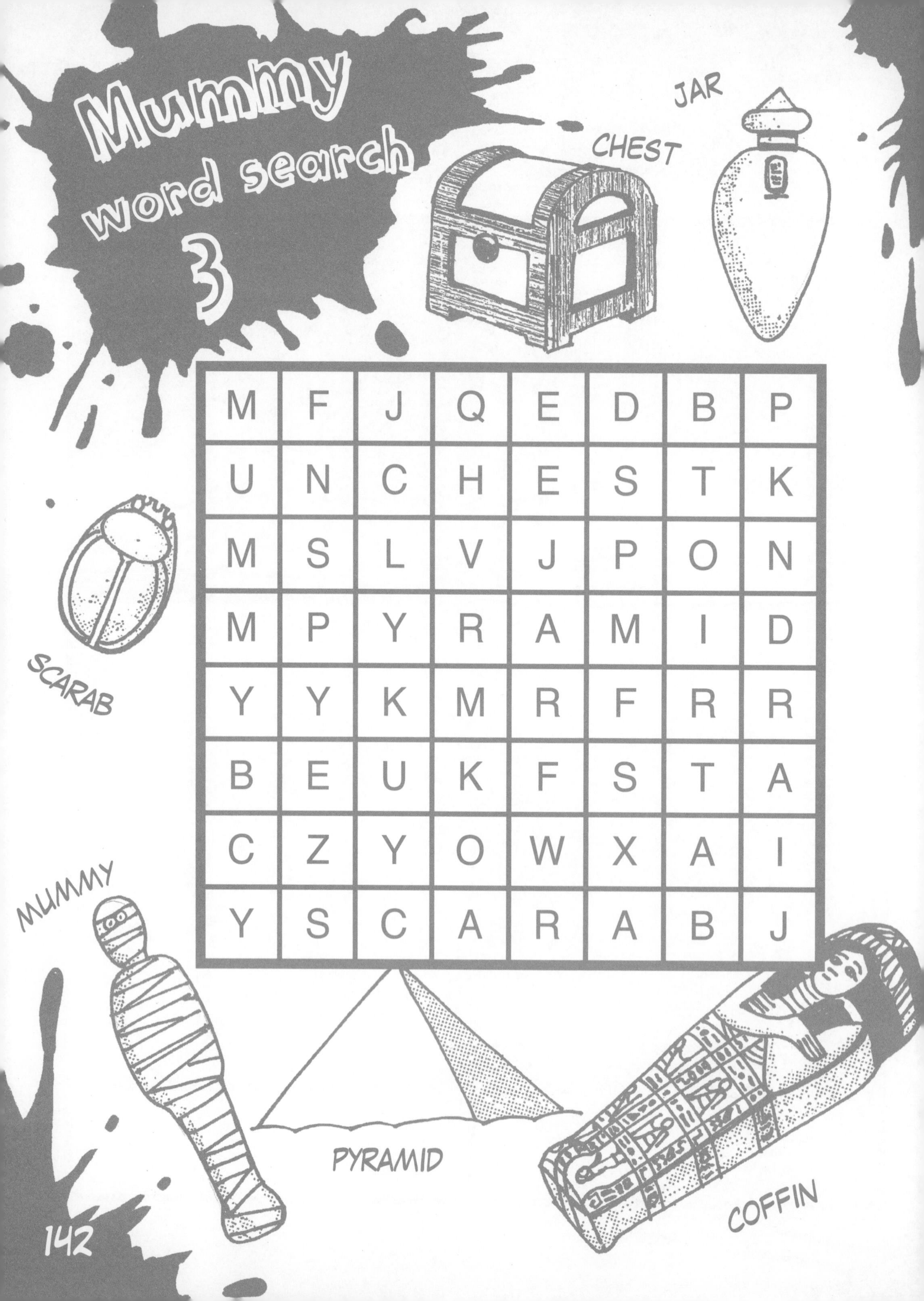

M	F	J	Q	E	D	B	P
U	N	C	H	E	S	T	K
M	S	L	V	J	P	O	N
M	P	Y	R	A	M	I	D
Y	Y	K	M	R	F	R	R
B	E	U	K	F	S	T	A
C	Z	Y	O	W	X	A	I
Y	S	C	A	R	A	B	J

Mummy crossword 1

USE THE CLUES TO FIT THE WORDS INTO THE CROSSWORD

WHERE A MUMMY IS BURIED

T _ _ _

A WRAPPED UP BODY

_ _ M _ _ _

LUCKY CHARM

A _ _ _ _ _ _ _

_ Y _ _ _ _ _ D

TRIANGULAR BUILDING

EGYPTIAN PAPER

_ _ P Y _ _ S

EGYPTIAN KING

P _ _ _ _ _ _ H

How to draw a manic mummy

joke!

Q: What did the mummy say when he heard a silly joke?

A: "That joke sphinx!"

Match the Egyptian figures to their silhouettes

Use the objects as clues to help you match

splat-a-match

Find the sarcophagus

How many scarab beetles can you find?
A-maze-ing!

Write the story

1

2

3

4

Splat-a-Fact

SADLY, MANY MUMMIES WERE DESTROYED WHILE BEING UNWRAPPED FOR "ENTERTAINMENT."

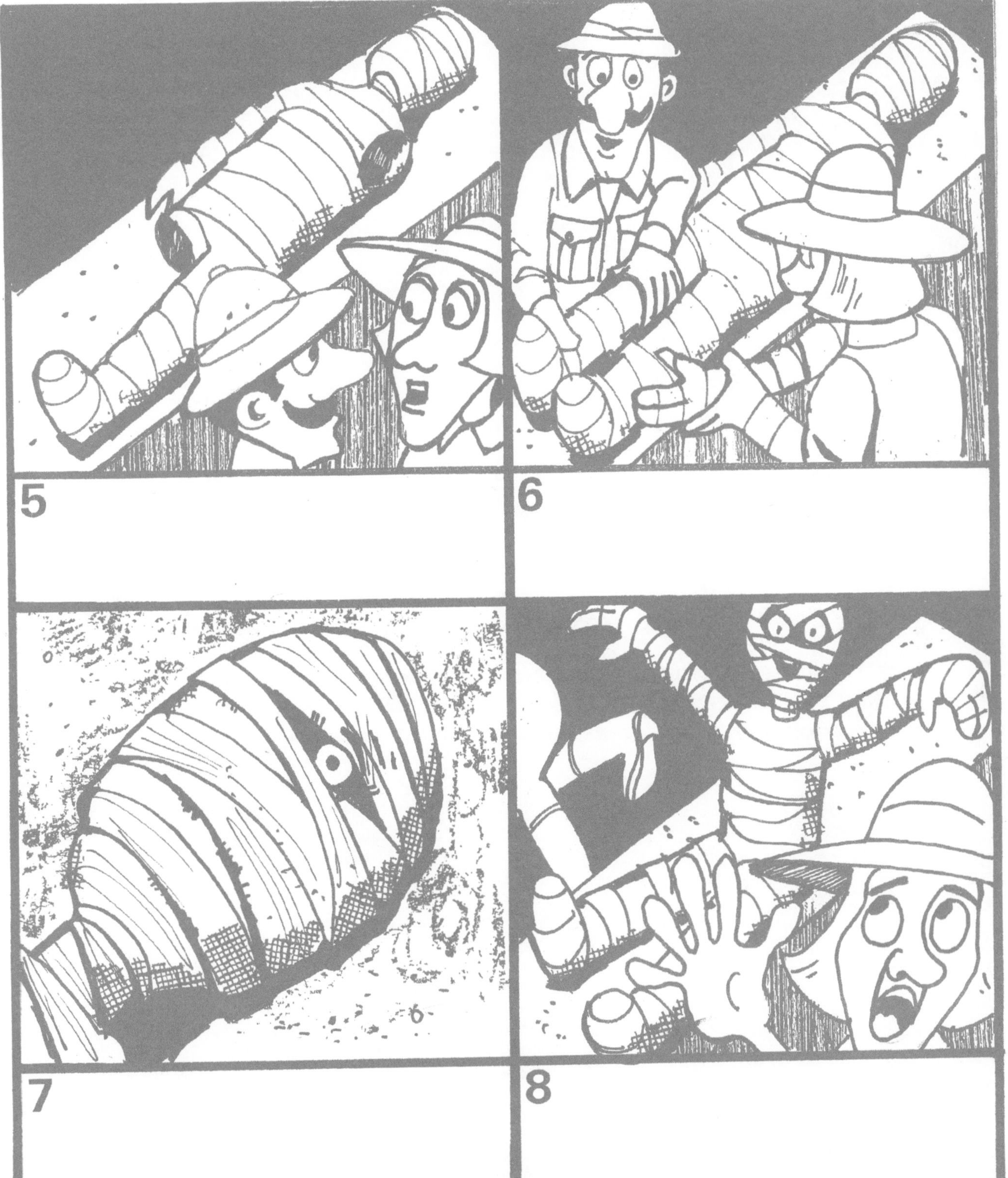

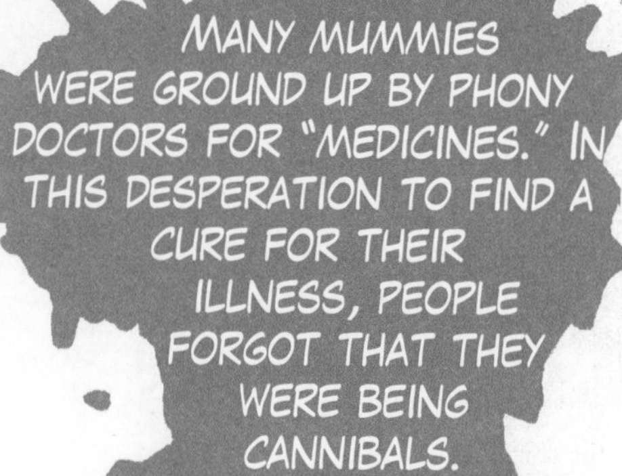

Many mummies were ground up by phony doctors for "medicines." In this desperation to find a cure for their illness, people forgot that they were being cannibals.

Splat-a-Fact

Help me find the mummy at the end of the maze!

Splat-a-Fact

The pharaoh was the chief priest of all the temples in Egypt and had a special relationship with the gods. His people believed that he was the son of Ra, the sun god.

A priest dressed as the jackal-headed god Anubis supervised the wrapping of the body. Jackals are scavengers and eat dead bodies, which is important in hot climates because otherwise bodies would rot and cause disease.
Splat-a-Fact
Remember me and draw me on the next page

Draw the mummy from the previous page from memory

splat-a-math
Mummy Sudoku 2
MAKE SURE THE NUMBERS 1, 2, 3, AND 4 FIT INTO EVERY ROW AND COLUMN.

4		1	
	1		4
	3		2
2		3	

How to draw a sarcophagus
1
2
3
joke!
Q: Why did the Italian say when he opened the sarcophagus?
splat-a-draw
156

4

DRAW YOUR OWN HERE

Where are my legs?
FINISH THE DRAWING OF THE SUN GOD RA!

DRAW ME WALKING LIKE AN EGYPTIAN!
EYE OF HORUS

There's been a mummy mix-up!
CAN YOU HELP PUT THE MUMMIES IN THE RIGHT COFFINS?
Q: What is a mummy's favorite flower?
joke!

A: Chrysanthemummies!

Battle of the Gods
Seth
GOD OF CHAOS,
CONFUSION AND
VIOLENT WATER
WHO WILL
WIN?

splat-a-battle
Horus
PROTECTOR OF EVERY PHARAOH
WRITE BELOW THE GODS THEIR SPECIAL POWERS, FIGHTING SKILLS AND STRENGTHS!
FIGHT!

CHEST
STOOL
FOOD
SERVANT FIGURES (SHABTIS)
HOW MANY TOMB GOODS CAN YOU FIND?
WE KNOW FROM PHOTOGRAPHS THAT EVERYTHING SHOWN ABOVE WAS IN TUTANKHAMEN'S TOMB WHEN CARTER FOUND IT.
Splat-a-Fact

Splat-a-Fact
Boats played such an important part in the lives of the Egyptians that they were sometimes put in tombs.

Which way?
I'm a mummy, get me out of here!

EXIT
Help me!

Mecha mummies
ROARRR
Yikes!

splat-a-draw
DRAW YOUR OWN ROBOT HERE

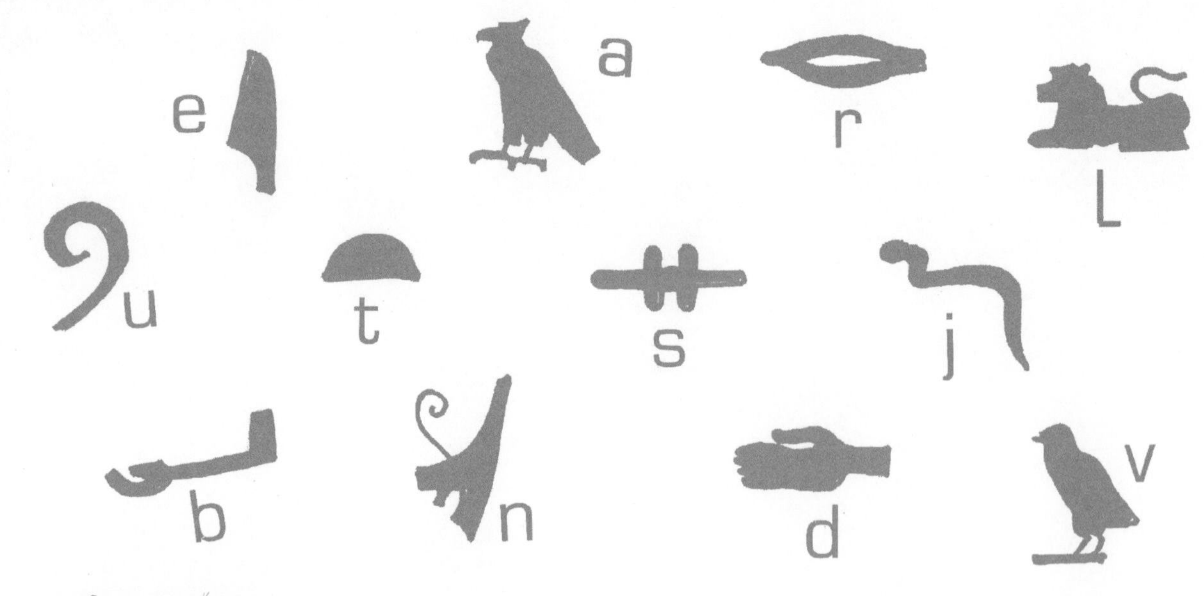

Splat-a-Fact

LEGEND HAS IT THAT GEORGE WASHINGTON (1732-99), FIRST PRESIDENT OF THE UNITED STATES, WORE FALSE TEETH MADE OF WOOD. ACTUALLY, THEY WERE MADE FROM HUMAN AND ANIMAL TEETH. HUMAN TEETH WERE OFTEN OBTAINED FROM CORPSES, OR FROM THE MOUTHS OF THE VERY POOR, WHO SOLD THEM.

PUT ME BACK TOGETHER!
Splat-a-Fact
IN JANUARY 2005, EGYPTIAN RESEARCHERS CARRIED OUT A CT SCAN THAT PRODUCED 1,700 IMAGES OF TUTANKHAMEN'S MUMMY. THEY FOUND THAT HIS LEFT THIGHBONE HAD BEEN FRACTURED AND BECAME SEVERELY INFECTED JUST BEFORE HIS DEATH.

Put the bones back together to make an x-ray mummy
Hmmm

Mummy crossword 2

MUMMY

KNIFE

AXE

TEMPLE

SWORD

CHARIOT

Word search 4

C	H	A	I	R	D	Y	N
R	O	C	K	E	T	A	M
S	L	M	L	A	M	P	O
R	J	Q	P	E	P	K	B
T	O	L	C	U	F	R	I
Y	V	A	N	Z	T	A	L
G	P	W	J	S	R	E	E
S	U	O	A	N	I	B	R

Mix up humans and animals!
Splat-a-Fact
QUEEN HENUTTAWY'S MUMMY WORE A WIG MADE OF BLACK STRING. SHE HAD SO MUCH STUFFING IN HER CHEEKS THAT HER FACE EXPLODED!

DRAW YOUR OWN MIXED-UP MUMMY!

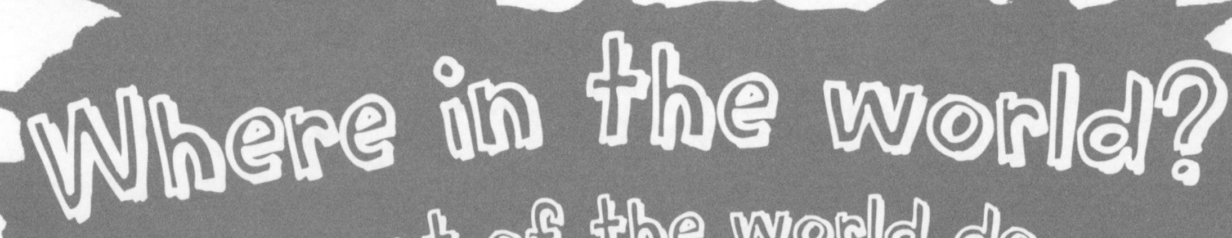

Where in the world?

Which part of the world do these mummies come from?

A

GREENLAND MUMMIES

B

THIS ANDEAN MUMMY WAS PROTECTED BY A CAIRN OF STONES.

C

THE FRANKLIN EXPEDITION EXPLORERS DIED IN 1845.

D

SOME SOUTH AMERICAN PEOPLES PRESERVED THE HEADS OF ENEMIES.

E

ANICENT INCAS ARE BELIEVED TO HAVE SACRIFICED CHILDREN

1

2

3

4

5

USE THE LETTERS AND NUMBERS TO MATCH UP EACH OF THE MUMMIES WITH WHERE THEY WERE FOUND IN THE WORLD.

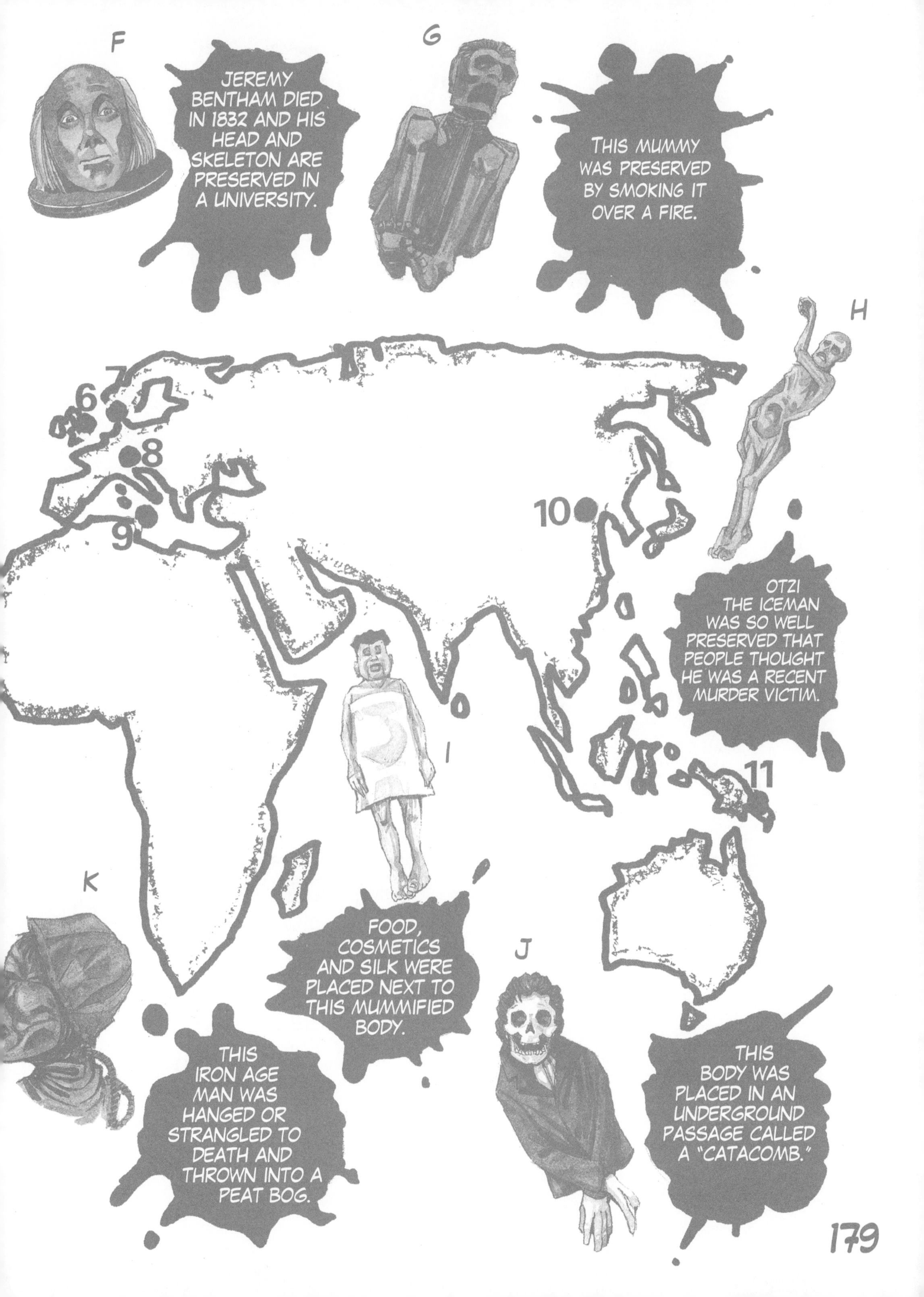
F
JEREMY BENTHAM DIED IN 1832 AND HIS HEAD AND SKELETON ARE PRESERVED IN A UNIVERSITY.
G
THIS MUMMY WAS PRESERVED BY SMOKING IT OVER A FIRE.
H
6
7
8
9
10
11
OTZI THE ICEMAN WAS SO WELL PRESERVED THAT PEOPLE THOUGHT HE WAS A RECENT MURDER VICTIM.
I
FOOD, COSMETICS AND SILK WERE PLACED NEXT TO THIS MUMMIFIED BODY.
K
THIS IRON AGE MAN WAS HANGED OR STRANGLED TO DEATH AND THROWN INTO A PEAT BOG.
J
THIS BODY WAS PLACED IN AN UNDERGROUND PASSAGE CALLED A "CATACOMB."

ANSWERS

4/5 - WHICH BANDAGE WILL UNRAVEL THE MUMMY?

8/9 - WHICH BUTTON BRINGS THE CREATURE TO LIFE?

10/11 - CAN YOU FIND TWO THAT ARE THE SAME?

12/13 - FIT THE WORDS INTO THE CROSSWORD

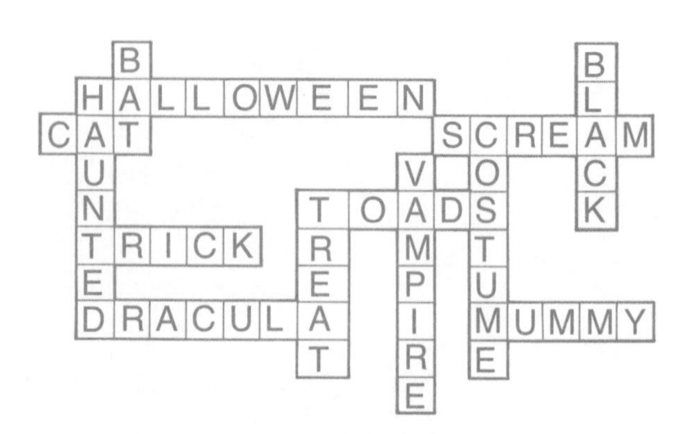

14/15 - HELP THE LITTLE DEVIL FIND HIS SWEETS

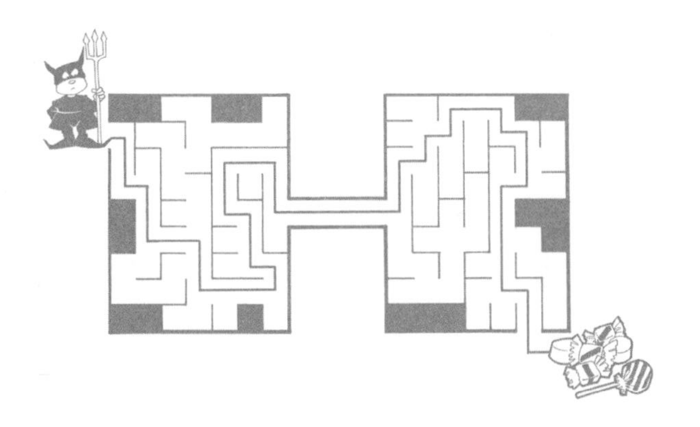

16/17 - BAT ATTACK! - MATCH THE IDENTICAL SILHOUETTES

18/19 - FIND THE TWO IDENTICAL VAMPIRE KIDS

20/21 - COUNT THE EXTRA SPOTS ON THE MUTANT PUMPKIN

23 ESCAPE THE MAZE

24/25 - PICK UP THE BONES IN THIS ORDER:

E, C, F, B, G, A, D

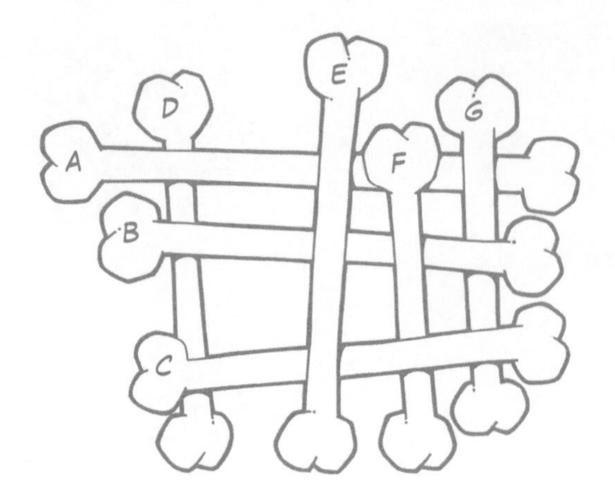

26/27 - SPOT THE DIFFERENCES 1

30/31 - SPOT THE DIFFERENCES 2

35 - COUNT THE VAMPIRE'S CANDY

THERE ARE 35 CANDIES

36/37 - UN-JUMBLE THE SPOOKY WORDS

OKPSOS
SPOOKS

TSIIPR
SPIRIT

MNAHPTO
PHANTOM

GLUOHS
GHOULS

THGSOS
GHOSTS

REPCES
CREEPS

38/39 - WHICH THREE TREATS ARE IN EVERY PICTURE?

42/43 - JOIN THE DOTS 1

44/45 - COUNT THE SNAKES

THERE ARE 6 SNAKES

50/51 - FIND THE MONSTER!

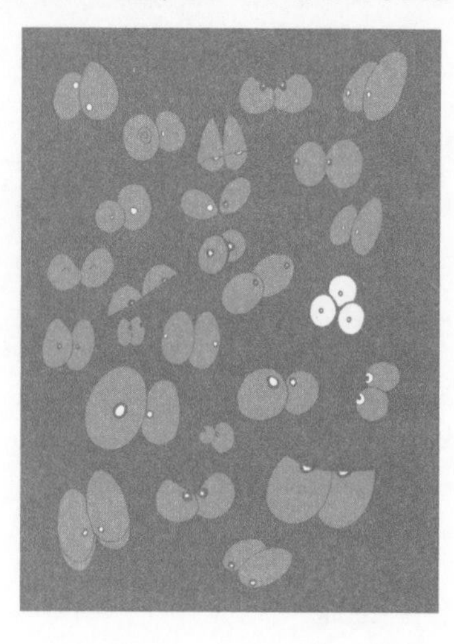

THERE ARE 24 OTHER MONSTERS HIDING IN THE DARK

52/53 - JOIN THE DOTS 2

54/55 - HELP THE MONSTER FIND HIS EYES

56/57 - COUNT WHAT'S IN THE JARS

20 EYEBALLS
17 WORMS
22 SLUGS
29 THUMBS

62/63 - WORD SEARCH 1

Y	W	O	P	B	E	R	I	M
L	I	E	T	S	A	E	N	U
R	T	R	R	K	C	T	E	M
E	C	I	P	E	Q	S	H	M
D	H	P	U	L	W	N	E	Y
I	L	M	S	E	D	O	R	F
P	L	A	S	T	R	M	L	K
S	C	V	T	O	A	D	R	F
R	Y	E	R	N	T	A	A	O

66/67 - REACH THE FLY BEFORE THE SPIDER!

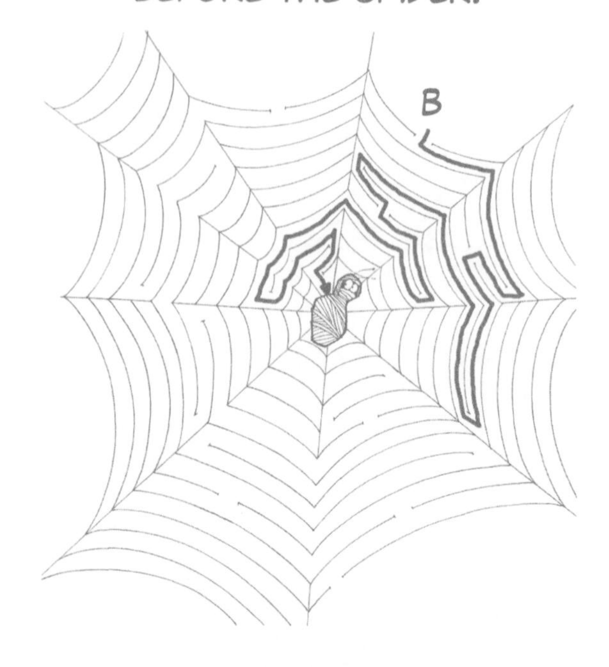

74/75 - UNSCRAMBLE THE WORDS

LDOCARUN
CAULDRON

BKOO FO LELSSP
BOOK OF SPELLS

BCALK TCA
BLACK CAT

YFINLG TCWIH
FLYING WITCH

TSIKOMOBRC
BROOMSTICK

CHITWS THA
WITCH'S HAT

70/71 - HOW MANY BATS IN THE BAT BOX?

76/77 - HELP THE RAT TO FIND HIS FLEAS

78/79 - SPOT THE DIFFERENCES 3

82/83 - ESCAPE FROM THE HAUNTED HOUSE

84/85 - MATCH THE TWO IDENTICAL SILHOUETTES

86/87 - WORD SEARCH 2

A	G	J	O	P	E	W	V	B	C
H	P	E	I	B	M	O	Z	E	G
P	W	H	S	T	N	M	K	E	A
R	K	E	A	C	O	L	O	G	R
Y	L	V	S	N	A	G	O	I	G
E	F	P	S	O	T	H	P	U	O
A	H	T	N	G	H	O	S	T	Y
B	E	R	D	W	Z	U	M	Y	L
R	V	U	I	D	G	L	J	Q	E
T	P	E	H	Z	B	E	S	A	C

92 - HIEROGLYPHS

93 - LEAD HORUS TO THE MASTABA

96 - MATCH THE MAGIC BRICKS

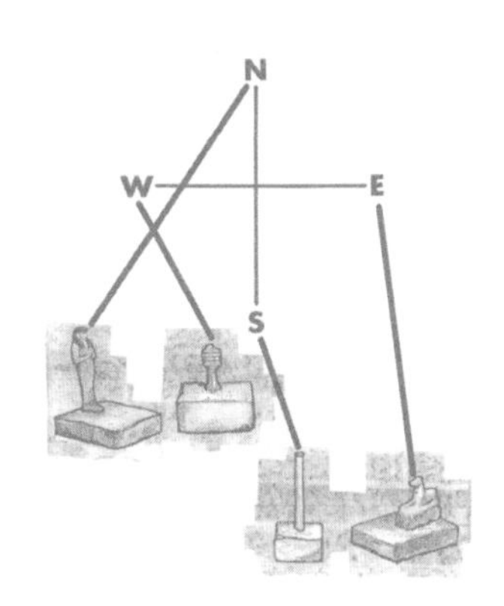

97 - MATCH THE ORGAN TO THE JAR

102/103 - SPOT THE DIFFERENCES

104 - MUMMY SUDOKU 1

1	2	3	4
3	1	4	2
2	4	1	3
4	3	2	1

105 - MUMMY MAZE

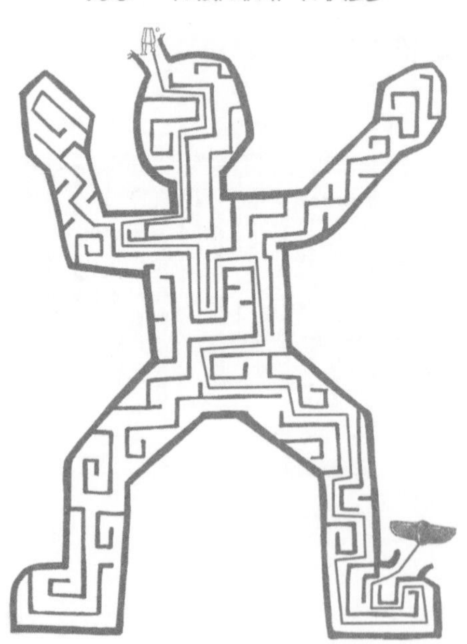

106/107 - MATCH THE ARTIFACTS TO THE BOXES

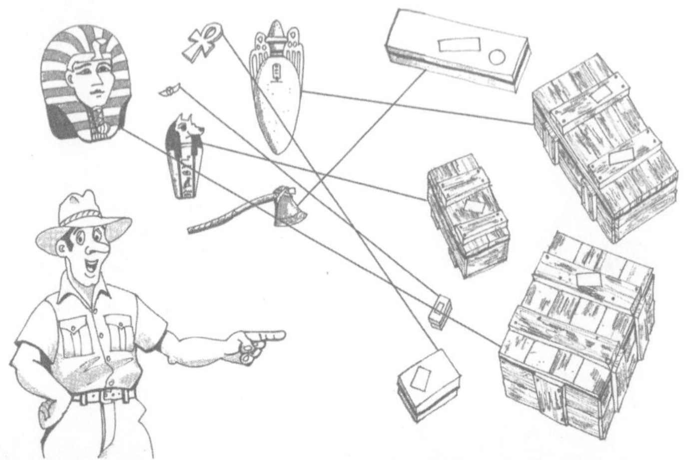

108/109 - HOW MANY SCARAB BEETLES IN THE TOMB?

ANSWER: 6

122/123 - HOW MANY MUMMIES CAN YOU FIND?

ANSWER: 40

115 - JOIN THE DOTS

132/133 - FIND THE MUMMY CASES

136/137 - LINK THE ANIMALS WITH THEIR MUMMIES

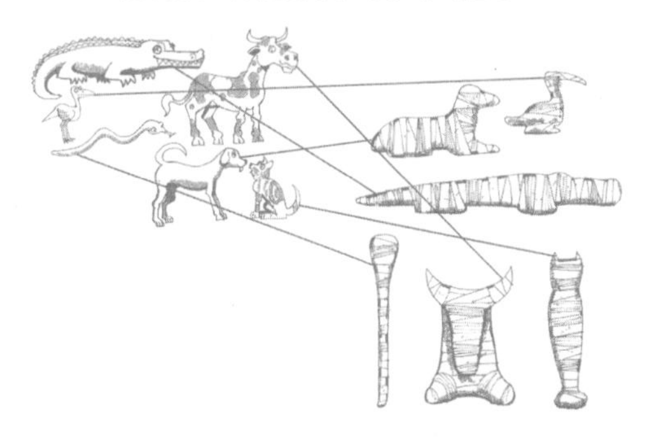

138/139 - HOW MANY MUMMIES IN THE TOWN?

ANSWER: 18

142 - WORD SEARCH 3

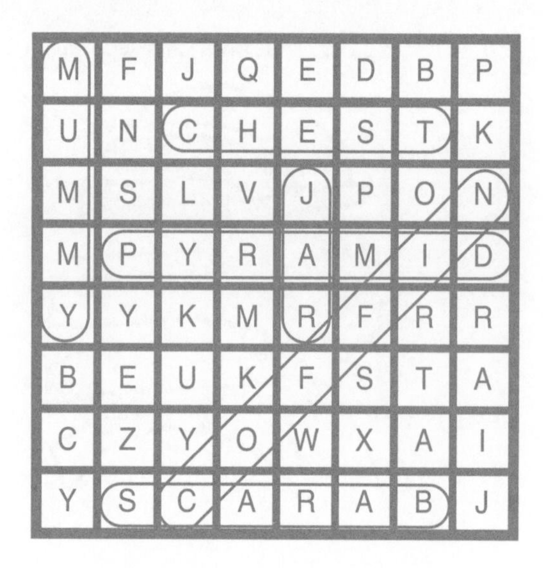

143 - MUMMY CROSSWORD 1

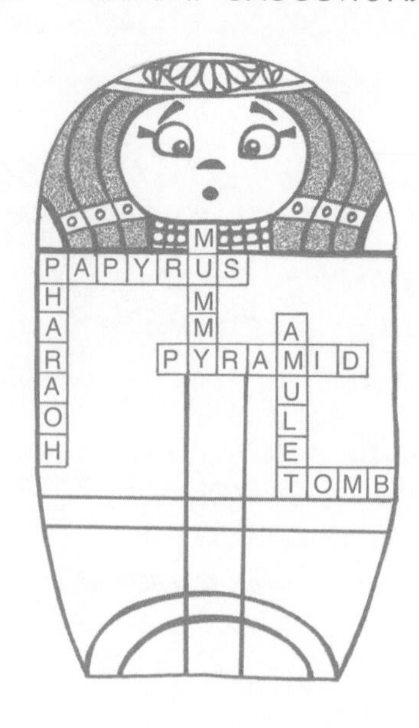

146/147 - MATCH THE EGYPTIANS TO THE SILHOUETTES

148/149 - FIND THE SARCOPHAGUS (THERE ARE SIX SCARAB BEETLES)

152 - HELP THE ARCHAEOLOGIST FIND THE MUMMY!

155 - MUMMY SUDOKU 2

4	2	1	3
3	1	2	4
1	3	4	2
2	4	3	1

160/161 - MATCH MUMMY AND SARCOPHAGUS

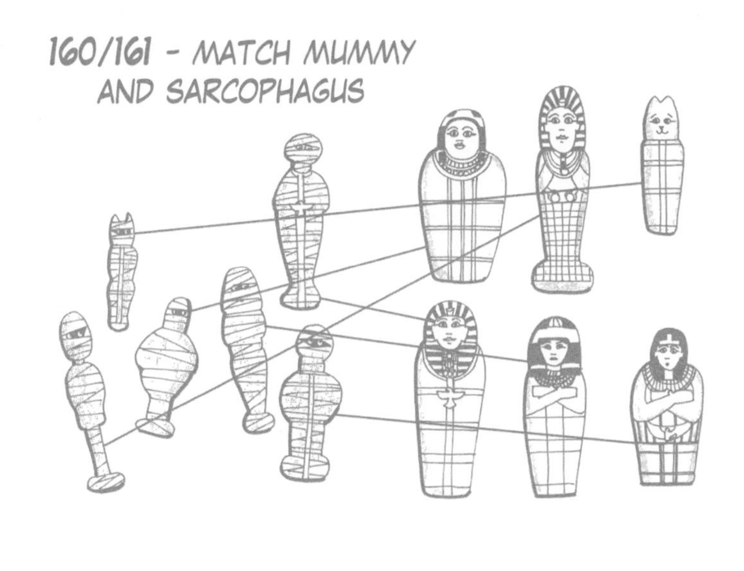

165 - FIND THE TOMB GOODS (THERE ARE TWELVE IN TOTAL)

166/167 - I'M A MUMMY, GET ME OUT OF HERE!

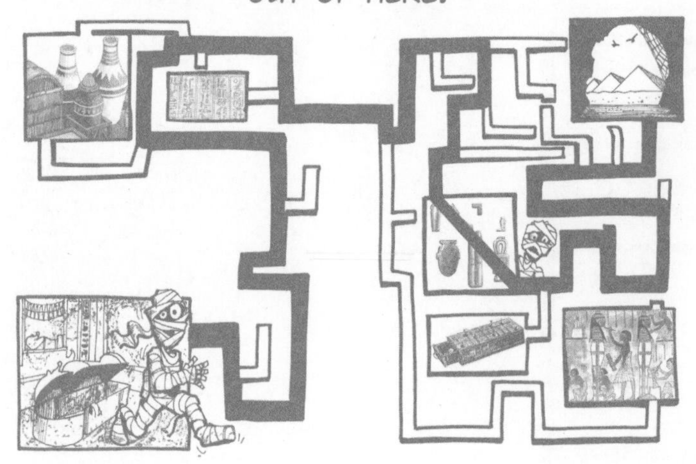

171 - FIND THE TOMB ENTRANCE

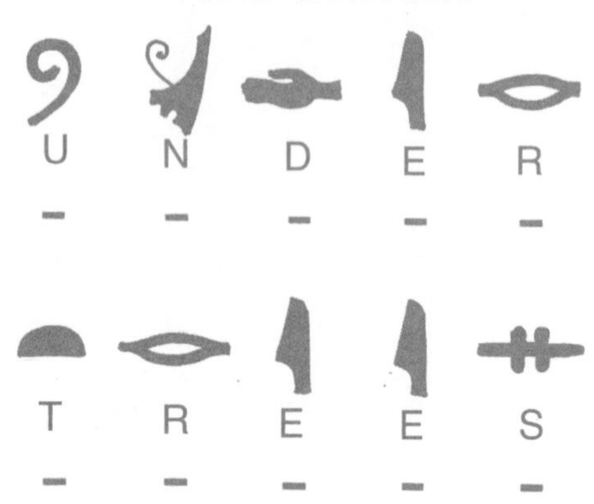

174 - MUMMY CROSSWORD 2

175 - WORD SEARCH 4

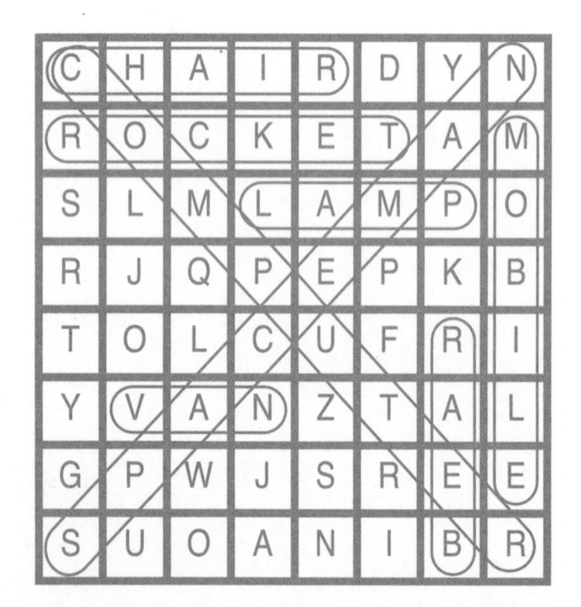

178/179 - WHERE IN THE WORLD?

1=C
2=D
3=B
4=E
5=A
6=F
7=K
8=H
9=J
10=I
11=G